Your Career After PLAB

Survival Tools for Young Doctors

Your Career After PLAB

Survival Tools for Young Doctors

Elitham B Turya MSc FRCPCH MBA
consultant in child health and mentor of young doctors

Edukom
www.edukom.co.uk

Edukom
5 Cambridge Close
Sale, Manchester
England M33 4YJ

www.edukom.co.uk
info@www.edukom.co.uk

First published by Edukom 2003
Reprinted 2003

ISBN 0- 9515819- 6- 1

Elitham B Turya
www.edukom.co.uk

Dear doctor

Congratulations on passing, or on gaining exemption from, PLAB. Now that the spectre of PLAB is over, how will you find your first medical job in the UK? Where are the guidelines on finding jobs?

To enhance you chances of securing medical posts you should learn how to write effective curricula vitae and acquire skills for winning at interviews.

'Your Career after PLAB' shows you how to present your qualifications, work history, experience and skills (your CV) to maximise your chances of being called for a job interview. It discusses the role of impressions *(appearance, speech/language and disposition)* at interviews.

I have used my experience as a foreign doctor, a job seeker, a mentor for doctors on clinical attachments and a recruiter to write this book.

'Your Career after PLAB' will explain and show you how to:
- Write letters
- Write your curriculum vitae
- Find a clinical attachment
- Apply for jobs
- Manage interviews
- Survive and thrive
- Write clinical documents
- Execute a clinical audit
- Write a research paper
- Use the internet.

It addresses the urgent teething problems faced by doctors new to the NHS, irrespective of the route used to arrive at her doors.

The stories are fictitious, the individuals named never existed.

I believe *'Your Career after PLAB'* will guide you to a rewarding career.

Yours faithfully,

EBTurya

Elitham B Turya

Acknowledgement

May I thank the young doctors who spent several weeks of clinical attachment with me. It is your questions and my attempts to answer them that lead to the writing of *'Your Career after PLAB'*. *Thank you.*

Thank you Abubakar Zubairu, Joanita Kigozi and Richard Lukambwa for ideas that enhance the impact of this book. Thank you for sharing my belief that doctors who enter British medical practice through the Preliminary Linguistic Assessment Board exams need guidance beyond *how (*to prepare*), how much (*does it cost*), where* and *when,* to sit PLAB exams.

Thank you Eva Asiimwe and Grace Mugisha, my language advisors, for criticising my grammar and my spelling, and for recommending that every chapter end with a summary.

I am indebted to Helen M Lewis for clarifying current play on training, research and 'dressing' for interviews.

Thank you, Mbabazi Anita, for designing the cover of the book.

Dedication

'Your Career after PLAB' is dedicated to all doctors (*and their spouses*) who have taken and passed PLAB, and must find work to earn a living.

You need the same degree of dedication and hard work as you study for, and sit membership exams of the royal college of your medical specialty.

May you find help in these pages.

Your Career After PLAB

Contents

1.0 What is your mission?

1.1 Why did you sit PLAB exams?

When you set out to prepare and take the PLAB exams you had a goal in mind. The goal may have been finding work that paid a better salary than in your homeland. You might have seen PLAB as a means of enabling you to eventually sit membership exams in your chosen specialty. Most likely you dreamed of both a better income and the membership of the Royal College of your specialty.

Preparing for, and taking PLAB was the easy part. From talking with friends, surfing the internet and writing to the GMC (www.gmc-uk.org), you found out what was needed and did it. The GMC sent you all you needed to know to sit for the examinations.

However, now that you have passed PLAB, reliable sources of advice, the internet and the GMC, have little or nothing to say about the next step, let alone how you should take it. What was once a clear route has faded and ended in a blind alley.

Light through alley is proved by *Induction Courses for International doctors*, paid for, and run by regional postgraduate deans over 2-3 days.

1.2 Induction Courses for International doctors

The course cover topics important to doctors new to Britain and the NHS. Topics covered include those listed below:

- NHS structure
- Living in the UK (banking, schools, housing, transport and sports
- Colloquial English
- Medical abbreviations
- Communication skills
- Immigration regulations
- Informed consent
- Death certification
- Prescribing and law
- Postgraduate medical education and training
- Examinations and study leave
- Junior doctors' hours
- How to get your next job
- Permit free training plus immigration
- Drugs and their doses
- Employment law
- Risk management
- Clinical governance

More information on *'Induction Courses for International doctors'* is available from:

NHS Professionals
Tel: 0845 1203167
Fax: 0114 2758008
e-mail: *lyndsay.towers@wymas.nhsprofessionals.nhs.uk*

1.3 Post- PLAB hurdles

If you want to become a principal general practitioner or a consultant in a hospital in the NHS, there are several more hurdles you must jump after PLAB.

You are eligible for limited registration (12 or 18 months initially). However you must get a job before you can exercise that eligibility.

• How shall you find your first job in the UK? If you get your first job, how shall you ensure that you continue to find jobs?

• What shall you do, as an SHO, to enhance your chances of getting a specialist registrar post?

• How shall you prepare for membership exams?

In the 1970s the GMC arranged clinical attachments for foreign doctors who sought work in Britain well before they left their home countries. On arrival in UK the doctors received a weekly allowance over the duration of clinical attachment (4 weeks). After the attachment they were helped to find jobs.

Now that the need and enthusiasm for foreign junior doctors has declined, you must find yourself a clinical attachment and pay for your subsistence. Once you pass PLAB, the GMC wants to hear from you only when you find a job.

1.4 Jumping the hurdles

The purpose of this book is to show you how to jump post-PLAB hurdles quickly and safely. The hurdles described are discussed in detail and practical suggestions are given.

1.4.1 Should you repeat internship?
Up to the late 1990s, it was relatively easy to find an SHO job if a doctor had done a clinical attachment in addition to passing PLAB. Recently the situation has changed. It is more difficult to get interviews for jobs after both PLAB and a clinical attachment. Many doctors have done several clinical attachments in the belief that it would improve their chances of getting an interview for a job.

Sorry doctor, repeating clinical attachments does not significantly increase your chances of getting an interview.

If I were in your shoes, I would either:
• Return home immediately, or
• Repeat internship (the pre-registration house officer year) in the UK.

1.4.2 Is returning home a viable option?
Are you free to return home? Refugee doctors do not have that luxury.

As an economic migrant, I would find returning home immediately a difficult option. How would I explain to my neighbours, that I, *doctor*, failed to find a job in England?

We must now examine *Option 2*: repeating internship.

1.4.3 Repeating internship in the UK
Repeating internship is rational on educational and financial grounds:

• It would enable you to *significantly improve your CV*. Recruiters want to know if the doctor has worked in the UK. Repeating internship would jump that hurdle. *With an improved CV*, you have a better chance of being called for a job interview.

• *You would learn how the NHS works* (or doesn't) much faster and better than you can from any number of clinical attachments.
• *You would ensure reliable references from consultants who knew you professionally* and could comment on your clinical knowledge and skills, your character and how you relate to colleagues and patients.

- *You would probably become more confident in answering questions* at interviews. After internship in the UK, you are probably more likely to get an SHO job and enter training and regular employment.

- *Repeating internship is cheaper than repeating clinical attachments.* You would get paid for your efforts £18,585/year or £1,548.75/month (January 2003). You could send a present to a favourite relative!

So, doctor, if I were younger, (only several years after my medical graduation), I would not hesitate in repeating internship.

1.4.4 What should a senior doctor do?
You may have been a senior registrar, a senior lecturer, a consultant, or a professor before your took the PLAB exams. Or if you came to Britain by special arrangement and the arrangements have not met your expectations, you have few options: you either return home or repeat internship in the UK, if you want to work as a doctor in the country.

What would I do? Sitting for PLAB meant that either I had no other means of securing employment as a doctor in Britain, I did not know about any alternative to PLAB or that I did not use them.

I would be unlikely to find a job of the same seniority as I had before coming to the UK. Local consultants are suspicious of the training and experience of foreign doctors. They would not give me a senior job, unless I was famous. I would not then be taking PLAB!

So, I would consider repeating internship. This would give me *local referees who would know me professionally* and *could comment on my clinical knowledge, skills, character and relationship to colleagues and patients.*

1.4.5 Pursue your goals
This book highlights the skills you should cultivate and nurture. The fruits of your efforts will be noted in the quality and content of your CV, the ease with which you complete job application forms and the confidence and clarity of your answers at interviews.

- You and you alone know why you came to Britain, why you took PLAB and what you want to achieve. How hard are you working towards your gaols?

- Nobody, not even your consultants, will make you master the writing of good letters and curricula vitae. You must learn on your own and practice until you are almost perfect!

- Beware of skills, knowledge and achievements that differentiate between doctors during short-listing and at interviews. These include clinical audits, courses attended, research, presentations, skills in resuscitation and life support, publications and the skills that make a doctor an asset to her/his clinical team (computer skills, leadership, personality, etc).

- Keep track of changes in the person specifications for senior clinical jobs. What is the trend? Optional or desirable attributes become mandatory as competition for jobs intensifies. Acquire some of these attributes as soon as possible.

- Attend courses, prepare for and take membership exams. If you don't, nobody will do it for you; nobody will force you.

Mind your English. You passed the English Language Testing System ELTS) before taking PLAB, I know. That was a sieve, to ensure you have essential language skills. As your medical knowledge and skills grow ensure that your fluency and literacy in English grow too. The way you write and speak English has strong strongly impact on your career.

To progress in your specialty you must demonstrate, not only that you are a good clinician, but also that you have done clinical audits, attended courses, trained in advanced life support, presented cases at meetings, taught somebody and may be even published something.

If you start early, it is easy to acquire most of these skills. If you do one audit every 6 months you will have six in 3 years. If you use your study leaves (2 weeks in 6 month) you will attend enough courses to enhance your education and CV.

The next chapter, *Writing letters*, describes how to write letters that do their jobs well, that transmit messages clearly and concisely. You will write many letters in pursuit of your personal and professional goals. Learn to write them concisely, precisely and politely so that they say what you want to say, not more and not less.

Clinical attachments may be done before part 1, after part 1 or after part 2 of PLAB. They are almost mandatory for doctors taking PLAB. During the attachment the doctor is introduced to the British health care system. The need for a clinical attachment is discussed and advice is given on finding one and getting the most out of it.

A clinical attachment helps a new doctor find a *mentor*, a senior doctor who, hopefully will listen, help solve problems, coach and act as a referee for the junior doctor.

How will prospective employers (hospitals and GP practices with jobs) know that you are an excellent doctor? You must learn how to inform them; and fast. That is the work of your *curriculum vitae* (CV) and *Covering Letter*.

Writing your CV, shows you, with examples, how to craft the tool for advertising (selling) yourself to potential employers. The need for and importance of a *covering letter* is examined and examples given.
The process of *applying for jobs* is succinctly described. If your CV and its covering letter have succeeded, you will be called for an *interview* to be seen and questioned by the people with jobs to give away. *Preparing* for, and *handling* the *interview* are discussed too.

When you secure your first job, you should do it so well that your consultant has no hesitation in recommending you, giving a good *reference*, for your next job.

1.5 Good medical practice
What should be done to enhance your career is examined in *Survive and thrive.* Elements of good clinical performance are detailed in the GMC's *Good medical practice (www.gmc-uk.org.uk):*

Good medical practice

History, physical examination and recognition of clinical signs
Does this doctor make an adequate assessment of the patient's condition based on the history and clinical signs and, if necessary, appropriate examination?

Providing or arranging investigations and treatment
Does this doctor provide or arrange appropriate and timely investigations and treatment? Is he/she competent when making diagnoses and when giving or arranging treatment?

Judgement & patient management
Is this doctor's judgement reliable? Does he/she show awareness of complications? Is his/her ward/out-patient management safe?

Does he/she recognise and work within the limits of his/her competence? Does he/she consult and seek advice appropriately?

Practical skills
Are this doctor's practical skills adequate?

Involvement of doctors and other health care professionals in providing clinical care:
Does this doctor consult colleagues and refer to other practitioners when indicated? Does he/she keep colleagues informed when sharing the care of patients?

Record keeping
Does this doctor keep clear, accurate and contemporaneous records which are adequate to inform others about the care of patients? Does he/she record relevant clinical findings, decisions made and information given to patients, and drugs or treatment prescribed?

Use of resources
Does this doctor pay due regard to efficacy and the use of resources?

Use of technology
Is this doctor competent in the use of IT which is necessary for patient care, such as information storage and retrieval systems?

Treatment in emergencies
Is this doctor willing and able to deal with common medical emergencies and with other illness in an emergency? Can he/she be relied upon to take prompt and suitable action within the limits of his/her competence and to seek assistance where necessary.

1.6 Non-clinical essentials

Other chapters deal with subjects that gradually become essential as your career progresses, or that ensure it does progress. Such topics include *clinical audits*, ***writing*** *clinical documents, reports, research papers* and *dissertations/theses.* Clinical work involves writing clinical letters and reports and an occasional medico-legal report. So learn to write them well.

Not every SHO or registrar will do research or write theses for higher degrees. These topics are included to give you an idea of what is expected *if* and ***when*** the opportunity arises.

Competence in the use of essential medical technology is recommended by the GMC.

Use of technology
Is this doctor competent in the use of IT which is necessary for patient care, such as information storage and retrieval systems?

The internet, that essential tool for rapid communication and gathering information, is introduced in ***Using the internet,*** the final chapter.

1.7 Further Reading

Each chapter in this book ends with '*Further Reading*'. I do not expect, no advise, you to buy each book cited. I hope however, that you will borrow and read many of them. Your hospital librarian will be happy to help you get some of them.

You have no excuse for not reading articles from the *BMJ*. Every British hospital library carries the *BMJ*. The *News* items in the *BMJ* are as informative and educational as the medical articles, to somebody new to British.

1.8 Are pastures greener in the USA?
Ever considered the USA and its *ECFMG* (Educational Commission for Foreign Medical Graduates) Certification, www.ecfmg.org? The exams cost money too. The USA *gives Visas **after** firm job offers.*

Summary
• Why did you come to Britain and why did you sit the PLAB exams?

• After PLAB, there are no handbooks or websites to advise you on what to do next. Talk to doctors *who have done it* before you. Find a mentor.

• If you need a clinical attachment, write directly to a consultant and ask her/him to help you. One clinical attachment should be enough.

• Repeating internship enables the doctor to meet local consultants who can reliably give references about your clinical knowledge, skills, character and relationship with colleagues and patients.

• *Mind your business.* Nobody is expected, or paid to look after your interests. That is your duty.

Further Reading

1. Hutton-Taylor S. **Marketing yourself as an overseas doctor**. *BMJ* 2002; 324: aa75.

2. Spillane M. **Branding Yourself:** how to look, sound and behave your way to success. Pan Macmillan: London 2000

4. GMC. **Good Medical Practice. 3rd** edition, May 2001

5. Swierczynski M. **Induction courses for international doctors.** *BMJ Career focus* 2002; 325: s159.

2. Writing Letters

2.1 Why write?
Writing letters and reports is an important part of a doctor's professional life. So learn how to write letters that do their jobs well. Learn to say what you want to say- no more, no less.

My letters are usually brief and factual. I write to keep in touch with friends and relatives, for business and professional purposes. My letters have objectives, aims and functions.

Your letter should say what you want it to say; no more, no less.
- think of what you are going to say and how you will say it
- write politely; there is no need to record your rudeness
- avoid ambiguity, your message should be clearly understood
- use clear simple words, avoid jargon wherever possible
- use short words, short sentences, and short paragraphs
- avoid superfluous professional jargon.

2.2 Do you have to write?
Letters are often kept by individuals and definitely by most business, governmental and educational organisations- at least for a while. Sometimes letters are scanned and kept on computers. Do you want you message on long-term record? Then make it clear, concise and precise.

When dealing with large organisations it is best to put your considered case in writing. However you must think carefully before writing. Write, read, and rewrite your letter till it says what you want it to say and nothing else. You may not be able to retract and amend it later.

A letter may be used as evidence in case of disagreement. It may support your case or it may be used against you.

Do you need to write that letter?
Have you talked with those involved? Can you get what you want without writing? If you must write (and often you must), then do it well.

2.3 Structure of a letter

A letter has several distinct parts (writer's address, date of writing, addressee's name and address, greeting, the message, closing phrase, writer's signature and name, and in organisations, the writer's official position) and each part has a function.

2.3.1 The writer's address

This is where the reply should be sent. The address should include post-codes, zip codes or post office box numbers as appropriate. The writer's address may be:

(a) *a post office box number and location* -*[Bank of Uganda, PO Box 7120 Kampala, Uganda]* mail for the bank is placed in numbered box in a post office in Kampala (to be collected by a messenger; **or**

(b) *the premises* (private or public) -*[Bank of England, Threadneedle Street, London EC2R 8AH]*- the mail is brought to the building and put into a receptacle or handed to a receptionist.

Post codes and Zip codes

Delivering mail (letters, parcels) in developed countries is facilitated by suffixes to the address- *post codes (zip codes in USA)*. These are combinations of letters and digits added to the address. They aid in sorting and delivering mail. Examples:
• Bank of England, Threadneedle Street, London EC2R 8AH.
• Microsoft Corporation, 1 Microsoft Way, Redmond WA 98052-6399.

EC2R 8AH is the format for post codes in Britain and *WA 98052-6399* is the style for *zip codes* in the USA.

If you do not provide a full address, you may not get a reply.

2.3.2 The date of writing

This fixes the letter in history. The date is important in business and legal transactions. When was the letter written? When was the order made, dispatched, or paid for? When was the promise or contract made?

2.3.3 References

References (**Your Ref., Our Ref.**) are vital in business and official letters.

They relate the letter to other communications (what was done, ordered, agreed, refused, postponed, contracted, bought, etc). They assist in retrieving relevant files and letters.

Official letters may also contain the initials of the officer responsible for the letter and of the secretary who typed it- EBT/MS. These too assist in handling queries arising from the letter. *Who knows about this? Who made the decision?*

Order Number, Invoice Number

Business letters may also quote **Order Number,** or **Invoice Number,** when referring to orders and invoices for the purchase or sale of goods. The numbers are needed in the handling, dispatch and payment for goods. Their use speeds up business transactions. Quote them appropriately in your business letters.

2.3.4 The addressee's *(receiver's)* name *and/or* official title

The name of the addressee- individual or officer to whom the letter is directed (the receiver), should be included. This speeds up official communications, ensuring that the letter goes straight to the right officer.

You should at least find out the title of the officer handling the subject of your interest. Do not write to huge organisations and hope that somebody will pass it to the right person. That may not happen.

Even when you know the officer's name, it is wise to include the official title. Your letter may arrive after the individual has gone on holiday or left the post. The deputy or successor will answer official letters (if the office is indicated), but may not touch what appears to be personal communications.

Common forms of address

Examples of words/phrases used to start common official letters are listed below.

Dear Sir, Dear Judge, The Hon. Mr. Justice (high court judges)
The Clerk (of the court, town, district, council
The Permanent Secretary (government ministries)
The Manager (bank, hotel, building society sporting teams, etc)
The Managing Director (business company, parastatal body)

The Director (bureau, centre, foundation, museum, gallery, etc.)
The Registrar (births, deaths, marriages, tribunal, university, etc.)
The Dean (diocese, university, academic faculties, diocese)
The Officer-in-Charge (armed forces unit, police unit)
The Secretary (commissions, foundations, committees, clubs, etc)
The President, (republic, chambers of commerce, union, etc.).

2.3.5 The addressee's (receiver's) address
The residential or postal address to which the letter is sent should also be included, particularly in business and official letters.

BMJ Bookshop	*The Medical Director*
BMA House	*Mulago Hospital*
Tavistock Square	*PO Box 7051*
London WC1H 9JR	*Kampala*
United Kingdom	*Uganda.*

Did I hear you say that you will write the address on the envelope? Envelopes are often thrown away after removing the letter. So include the addressee's name and address on the letter too.

Personal letters often omit the receiver's address. It is better to include it unless you are writing to close friends and relatives. If you are not sure, include it.

2.3.6 The greeting
A greeting is used to start a letter, to greet the receiver. It is pure and simple politeness, like saying *Good morning* to somebody when you don't care whether his morning is good or terrible.

Dear Sir, Dear Madam, Dear Mr. Ghandi, Dear...are typical phrases used to start letters. The word *Dear* does not mean the addressee is a loved friend or relative. Letters to enemies also start with *Dear*....

2.3.7 Re: Subject:
Business and official letters should have headings to the body of the letter. This states the subject of the letter. Headings may start with **Re:** (in the matter of) or with **Subject.**

Re: *Application for the post of senior house officer*
Subject: *Application for the post of senior house officer*

In the past the heading was underlined: <u>Re: Financing study leaves.</u>
Heading are now highlighted (*darker letters*): **Re: Financing study leaves**.

Heading are useful in directing the letter to the right officer dealing with the subject/problem. Some organisations and individuals get so many letters that untitled communication risks getting lost in paper piles.

Headings are helpful in sorting, filing and retrieving letters. So give your letter a title. If you know what you are writing about, this is a simple job.

2.3.8 The message
This is the reason for writing the letter. If you want somebody to understand and act on the basis of your letter, then give him or her the full picture. Write clearly and concisely giving facts and details so that the reader gets your *message.*

So before you put pen to paper or touch the computer keyboard, *think:*
• What do you want to say?
• How do you like to say it?
• What would you like to leave out of the letter?
• What would you wish to know if you received such a letter?

2.3.9 The closing phrase (signing off)
A friendly phrase is used to end letters. In business and official letters the closing phrase is usually one of the following:

> *Yours sincerely* (if the letter started with a personal name)
> *Yours faithfully* (if official titles only was used)
> *Your obedient servant* (by a junior official to a senior, rarely used now).

These phrases have nothing to do with sincerity, faithfulness (trust), obedience or servitude. They are simple historical remnants of English politeness, no more and no less. Polite letter writers use them.

Phrases that end letters to relatives and close friends include:
Your affectionate (daughter, son, etc)
Yours affectionately
With love
Your (son, niece, etc.)
Yours.

Keep these for letters to relatives and close friends. They are impolite when used in letters to strangers or official communications.

2.3.10 Writer's signature and name
The writer's signature and printed name should follow the closing phrase. Do you want your letter answered? Make it easy- print your name below your signature.

Yours sincerely,

J Mukhtar

Jamil Mukhtar

2.3.11 Official title/ position/ office
In business and official letters, it is standard practice to indicate the writer's position in the organisation.

Yours faithfully,

EM Mahon

Eric M Mahon

Associate Debt Manager

These titles are helpful to new recruits, outsiders or ,as commonly happens in large organizations, when it is not possible to associate every name with a position, rank or function. They are also helpful in subsequent telephone communications when somebody may ask, and they frequently do, *Who is she? What does he do here?*

2.4 Examples
The following three are examples of letters that could have been written by junior doctors looking for clinical attachments or jobs.

Dr Musoke seeks a clinical attachment in Urology.

Dr Kilunda Musoke
19 Dulwich Close
Sale M33 4ZP

Tel. 077 x74544 (mobile)

12 June 2002

Mr David Krypton
Consultant Urologist
Trafford General Hospital
Moorside Road
Urmston M41 5SL.

Dear Mr Krypton

Re: Request for a clinical attachment in Urology
My I request your help with a clinical attachment in your department. The attachment would enable me to observe clinical norms and gain insight into the working of the NHS. Would 8 weeks be adequate?

I have an MMed (Surgery) from Makerere University in Uganda and have passed the PLAB exams.

Details of my education, qualification and clinical experience are shown in the enclosed curriculum vitae.

Yours sincerely

KMusoke
Kilunda Musoke MB Mmed

2.4.2 Applying for a Pre-Registration House Officer post

17 Campion Close
Eccleshall
Stafford ST21 6SR

Tel 0773 74x44 (mobile)
uzomaobi@yahoo.co.uk

22 April 2002

Miss Petra Matthews
Human Resources Officer
Whipps Cross Hospital
Whipps Cross Road
Leytonstone
London E17 6EE

Dear Miss Matthews

Re: Application for a pre-registration house officer post in Medicine

May I apply for the post of pre-registration house officer in Medicine,
Ref. HO/M34, advertised on www.bmj.com on 17 April 2002.

I graduated in Medicine from the University of Nigeria in 2000, have
passed PLAB and completed an 8 week clinical attachment in Medicine.

I hope the job will give me a better knowledge of clinical practice in UK
before seeking SHO posts in Medicine.

Details of my education, experience and referees are in the enclosed CV.

Yours sincerely

UObiaya
Uzoma Obiaya MB BS

1.4.3 Applying for an SHO post

Dr Indra Shastri
218 Moorside Rd
Urmston
Manchester M41 5SL

Tel. 0161 747 976x
Ishridar@hotmail.com

2 November 2002

Personnel Officer
Bradford Royal Infirmary
Duckworth Lane
Bradford BD9 6RJ

Re: Application for post of Senior House Officer in Obstetrics and Gynaecology (Ref AOG 357).

I would like to apply the post of Senior House Officer in Obstetrics and Gynaecology advertised in the BMJ, 31 August 2002.

I have an MD in Obstetrics and Gynaecology, passed PLAB in June and Part 1 of the MRCOG in September 2002.

After obtaining the MRCOG, I hope to spend 2 years as registrar in reproduction medicine before returning to work in Kerela, India.

Details of my qualifications, clinical experience, publications and referees are shown in the enclosed curriculum vitae.

Yours faithfully,

IShastri
Dr Indra Shastri MB BS MD

Summary
- Follow the standard structure for letters
- Write politely; there is no need to record your rudeness
- Give enough details to enable the reader to respond as required
- Quote Reference/ Invoice/ Order/ Customer numbers for fast action
- Give headings or titles to business and official letters
- Use clear simple words, avoid jargon wherever possible
- Use short words, short sentences, and short paragraphs
- Avoid superfluous words and phrases
- Print your name below your signature in official and business letters.

Further Reading

1. Jarvie G. **Bloomsbury Grammar Guide**. Bloomsbury, London 2000.

2. Strunk W. White EB. **The elements of Style.** Longman, London 1999.

3. Writing Your CV

3.1 What is a curriculum vitae?
A curriculum vitae (CV) is a summary of an individual's professional life and work (personal details, qualifications, skills and experience, education, work history, hobbies and other interests). CVs (curricula vitae) are also called *Career Summaries, Biodata or Resume* in the USA.

3.2 Why do you need a CV?
The purpose of a CV is to inform a potential employer of your suitability for the job, to tell her/him what a good doctor you are. Your CV's job is to get you an interview with the employer or his representative.

When you apply for a job, your aim is to convince the recruiter that you are what he/she requires for the job. Like a vendor in an open market you display your goods (through your CV or at an interview) to your customer (the recruiter). Your qualifications, skills, experience and personality, [*YOU*], are on sale. In the market the best goods sell first. Similarly the best candidates are selected first (hopefully). Your duty is to present yourself as the best. Thus a good CV is an asset in the competition for jobs, research grants and training positions.

Your CV should be **clear, concise, precise, and simple.** The layout should make it possible for the reader to find information quickly.

Your CV can also be used:
• to apply for advertised jobs (accompanied by a covering letter)
• as a source of sorted information when completing application forms
• to inquire about future jobs (accompanied by a covering letter)
• to apply for training positions (accompanied by a covering letter)
• to apply for research grants (with research proposals and cover letters).

3.3 Structure of a CV
Curricula vitae are as different as the individuals they describe. However they follow a common format (*'Usual format for medical CVs', page 33).*

The CV should display personal details, qualification(s), career plans, education, work history, other relevant information (publications, prizes, IT skills, etc) and hobbies clearly.

The order in which the topics appear in the CV will vary slightly depending on individual preferences. However it is best to follow a standard format till you are more experience in writing CVs.

Senior doctors create separate sections in their CVs for clinical audit, teaching, research, publications, management and clinical governance. These activities become important with seniority. The subsections make it easier for the recruiter to find information about these roles.

3.3.1 Personal details
State your postal address, telephone number and e-mail address (if you have one). Give you full names, date of birth, nationality and sex.

3.3.2 Qualifications
State your qualifications (BSc, MB ChB, MD, etc). Memberships (by examination) of professional bodies (MRCP, MRCS, MRCGP, etc) are included in this section. Passes at parts/modules of professional examinations should be listed separately and clearly identified as such. Do not claim full qualifications after passing part 1! The recruiter will not be impressed.

Failed exams
Some doctors include in their qualifications: MRCP part 2 (failed), or something similar. I do not understand nor approve of such 'naivety'. Don't list examinations you have failed.

If you have passed part of a membership exam recently then mention it. Say when you are siting the next part. If you passed part 1 several years ago, do not list it. "Shall he ever get the membership? No. Reject."

3.3.3 Career plans
Briefly state your future plans and how the job will help you achieve them. Your reason for applying for the job should be on the front page in the Career Plan. You may have worked in different specialties before finding

Usual format for medical CVs.

Short name (*Initials* and **surname** and *major qualification*)
Address:

Telephone (day time):
Fax:
E-mail:

Full Name (*first name(s) followed by SURNAME*)
Date of birth:
Nationality:
Sex:

QUALIFICATIONS
State your qualification(s) dates, institution (college/ university).

CAREER PLAN
Briefly state your plans and how the job will help you achieve them.

EXPERIENCE AND SKILLS
Concisely list your main skills and abilities.

EDUCATION
Give dates, name and location of institutions, subjects studied and
qualifications gained. Mention outstanding non-academic achievements
(leadership roles, prizes and distinctions) too.

WORK HISTORY
Dates, position held, employer's name and location, main duties and
achievements.

ADDITIONAL INFORMATION
Useful facts that do not fit well into the above categories may be mentioned
here: relevant courses attended, and useful skills acquired.(*Omit this section
if you have no additional information to give*).

INTERESTS (HOBBIES)
Name and briefly describe your hobbies and leisure activities.

your niche. Your *Career Plan* should be short and clear. Think about what you intent to achieve before writing the plan. Examples:
- I plan to take the MRCP and specialise in Neurology
- My intention is to take the MRCS and specialise in Thoracic Surgery
- My plan is to gain the MRCPCH and specialise in Clinical Immunology.

NHS posts mix training and employment. The recruiter may want to know if the job will help you pass your exams in addition to paying you a living wage?

There is no need for long paragraphs, let alone full pages of personal statements. When I am short-listing I want to know why the candidate wants the job, not what he/she wanted as a teenager. So be brief, limit your plan to two lines.

3.3.4 Experience and skills

List your main skills and abilities concisely. The details will be in the *'work history'* section of the CV. The aim of this section is to highlight what the employer would get if she employed you. Examples:
- 3 years of neonatal and paediatrics at SHO level in a regional hospital
- supervised and taught medical students and house officers in surgery.

This section is more useful the senior the candidate with long careers. PRHO and SHOs can afford to omit this section. Their CVs are short enough and need no summarising.

3.3.5 Education

Give the dates, names and addresses of the institutions you attended, courses taken and examinations passed. Outstanding non-academic achievements too should be described briefly (class president, head prefect, athletics captain, president of debating society, etc) with dates.

3.3.6 Work history

Give dates, job titles, names of employers and location, and your duties and responsibilities. Briefly state your achievements in each position.

Employers are interested in what you have done (and can do), and not *empty years of experience.* Example:

---

*July 1998 - June 1999: **Registrar in Paediatrics,*** St Johns Hospital, Essex:
- inpatient and outpatient hospital paediatrics and neonatal medicine
- taught clinical skills to medical students and senior house officers
- completed, presented and published two clinical audits (*see Audit*).

Of course you could write the above as full sentences in a continuous paragraph. However important achievements would not stand out of the prose. Make it easy for the recruiter to notice your main skills and achievements.

3.3.7 Research and Publications

If you have done any research and published papers cite them. If you have contributed chapters to books or written whole books include them here. List your publications: author(s) names, title of book, city/town in which published, publisher and year. Give title of the journal, date, volume and pages; follow the Vancouver style for citing references. Examples:

Citing a published book:
Jarvie G. **Bloomsbury Grammar Guide**. London: Bloomsbury 2000.

Citing a paper published in a journal:
Hutton-Taylor S. **Marketing yourself as an overseas doctor**. *BMJ* 2002; 324: S75.

3.3.8 Interests/ hobbies

The purpose of this section is to show that you have a life outside medicine. Name and briefly describe your hobbies and leisure activities. If you are a member of a competitive sport team, say so. Your role in community activities, charity groups, your religious community or any other social group may be described here.

Do not include activities likely to offend prospective employers. Be sensitive in your choice of words.

3.3.9 Additional information

This is where you may state other information you wish the recruiter to know, but could not easily fit into the other sections.
- general and professional courses you have attended, or are attending
- special professional, linguistic, technical (computing) skills, etc.

3.3.10 Referees

These are people who know you socially, from university or college or from work who are able and willing to commend you to a new employer. Ask them if they would be willing to act as your referees.

List names, addresses, telephone and fax numbers of 2 or 3 people who have *agreed* to be give references on your character and skills. Do not name anybody if he has not agreed to do so. He may refuse to send a reference or worse, send a bad one.

Use people who will put in a good word for you. *If you think a particular person will give you a bad reference do not use him as a referee.* Why would you commit professional suicide?

3.4 CV types

A CV may take three slightly different formats: *Targeted, Chronological* and *Functional.*

3.4.1 A targeted CV names the target job (what the applicant is aiming for), states his capabilities (skills) and summaries his work experience.
The applicant:
- gives personal details (names, date of birth, sex, etc)
- lists academic qualifications and other accomplishments
- gives his work experience while at school or college, and after
- names and briefly describes hobbies and other interests, and
- gives names of referees.

A targeted CV is suitable for a young candidate who is looking for his first substantive job. It is ideal for non-professional graduates entering public services or business.

3.4.2 A chronological CV lists work experience from the first job to the last (most recent). Chronological CVs are suitable for candidates who want to stay in the same industry or profession, who have relatively short work records or have not changed jobs frequently.

3.4.3 A functional CV
By the time most doctors become registrars (let alone GPs principals or hospital consultants) they have changed jobs several times. A chronological CV would not display their skills and work history to their advantage. A functional CV is required to do their career justice.

A functional CV lists professional qualifications, highlights functional competencies (skills and expertise) and summarise of work experience from current or most recent position back to the first.

As responsibilities and achievements increase from house officer to registrar to consultant or principal GP, so does the length and complexity of the CV. Functional CVs are ideal for presenting the details most senior doctors want to include in their CVs.

Because doctors change jobs frequently it becomes tedious if the same details are listed under every post. With the passage of time (experience) it becomes desirable to highlight essential skills and experience to reduce the tedium of repeating identical job descriptions.

Functional CVs are appropriate for senior doctors (registrars looking for consultant jobs or consultants and GP principals changing employers or moving into management).

3.5 Preparing the CV
Many people are reluctant to write their CVs. They fear that they will get it wrong. You are now an expert walking, talking, reading and writing; you learnt to them, often with falls and amusing linguistic mistakes.

Writing CVs is a skill that must be learnt too. It is an essential marketing tool for most professionals who want to progress. So find time and the will to learn how to write your CV.

3.5.1 *Confusion about writing and typing*
Some doctors confuse *typing* a CV with **writing** one. By writing, I mean the creation of a summary of your professional life and work (personal details, qualifications, clinical experience, education, hobbies and other interests) into a persuasive document.

When a recruiter starts reading your CV you probably have less than two minutes to convince her/him of your suitability for the job. A good first impression is vital. Your CV should cast your personal and professional qualifications to meet the demands of the post.

3.5.2 *Composing a CV*
Composing a good CV takes time and effort. However given that the average doctor changes jobs at least three times within two years of graduation, that he/she will apply for several jobs before getting appointed to a position, any effort spent on composing a good CV is an investment– it will pay off.

To prepare your CV, follow *'Usual format for medical CVs'* on page 31. Write down under each heading all relevant information about you and your career

Unfortunately most CVs on the internet are not quite suitable examples for writing a medical CV. They are aimed at people seeking jobs in the private sector (business mainly). The format of medical CVs and degree of details expected are different from business CVs.

Follow *'Usual format for medical CVs'* and writing down as much as you can on every item in the format. Type (word-process) notes and then arrange it into a document whose *'look'* resembles the examples on page 39 and 41. Don not imitate their content, use them for the *'look'*

3.6 Examples of doctors' CVs
1. Dr Ghalib is looking for an SHO post in Orthopaedics (*page 39*)
2. Dr Chieke wants an SpR post in Infectious Diseases (*page 41*).

A M Ghalib MB BS

Address: 15 Kineton Close
                  Matchborough
                  Redditch B98 0EU

Telephone: 0152 7651547x
                  0776 896036x

Name: **Anwar Mohamed GHALIB**
Date of birth: 20th May 1972
Sex: Male
Nationality: Indian

QUALIFICATION
MB BS, June 1997, Osmania University, Warrangal, India.

Passed: PLAB, March 2001, Eligible for Limited registration, and
         part 1 of the MRCPCH, January 2002.

CAREER PLAN
I hope to work as an SHO in orthopaedics, obtain the MRCS, gain registrar
experience in Paediatric Orthopaedics then return to India.

EDUCATION
1991-1997: Kakatiya Medical College, Osmania University, MB BS course
- Dr Pulaparti Srinivas Gold Medal for best student in Surgery
- represented university at national university sports championships
- secretary to university athletics student council (1995-96).

CURRENT APPOINTMENT
*Sept 2001- to date: **Locum Senior House Officer in Orthopaedics,***
Redditch General Hospital
- 1st on call for orthopaedics, inpatient and outpatient clerking and
- investigating patients, securing patient consent for operations.

PREVIOUS APPOINTMENT

*[May-June 2001: **Clinical Attachment in Surgery**, Redditch General Hospital].*

Dec. 2000- March 2001: Preparing for and taking PLAB exams.

*Jan. 2000 - Nov. 2000: **Senior House Officer in Orthopaedic Surgery**, Osmania Hospital, Hyderabad, India.*
- 1st on-call for orthopaedic surgery and trauma medicine
- supervising medical students and house officers in orthopaedics.

*July 1998- Dec 1999: **Senior House Officer in Paediatrics**, Osmania General Hospital, Hyderabad,*
- on-call for paediatric and neonatal medicine and paediatric surgery

*July 1997- June 1998: **House officer**, Osmania General Hospital, Hyderabad,*
- 3 month in Medicine, Paediatrics, Obstetrics and Gynaecology and Surgery.

AUDIT

Delay in surgery for acute osteomylitis, Osmania Hospital, *July 2000.*
Delay in presentation delayed surgical treatment. 75 % osteomyelitides were treated on the day of addition and 90% within 48 hours.

ADDITIONAL INFORMATION
- Languages: fluent in Hindi, Punjabi and Gujarati.
- Computing and IT: skilled in desktop publishing.

HOBBIES
Playing squash and listening to Indian music.

REFEREES

Mr Hamid Khalifa FRCS
Consultant Orthopaedic Surgeon
Redditch General Hospital
Redditch B98 0EU

Tel: 0152 7951535x
Fax: 0152 7951576x

Mr Kevin Graham FRCS
Consultant Surgeon
Redditch General Hospital
Redditch B98 0EU

Tel: 0152 7951576x
Fax: 0152 7951577x

Dr E. Chieke MB BS MRCP

Address:	14 Campion Close
	Eccleshall
	Stafford ST21 6SR
Telephone	077 374x44 (mobile)
e-mail:	echieke@yahoo.co.uk
Name:	**Ebele Chieke**
Nationality:	Nigerian
Date of birth:	16th June 1969
Sex:	Female

PROFESSIONAL QUALIFICATIONS
MB ChB, December 1997, University of Benin, Nigeria
MRCP, July 2001, Royal Colleges of Physicians, UK

PROFESSIONAL BODIES
Full Registration with the GMC
Member of the Medical Defence Union
Member of the Royal College of Physicians of London.

CAREER INTENTION
I would like to specialise in Medicine, obtain the CCST in General Medicine with an interest in Infectious Diseases.

SKILLS AND EXPERIENCE
- *General medicine* experience and skills in tropical medicine, cardiology, nephrology, endocreinology, respiratory (asthma, chronic bronchitis, tuberculosis), gastroenterology and geriatrics

- *Teaching skills:* taught medical students, and senior house officers in using traditional and problem based learning methods.

- *Audit experience* from clinical audits performed and presented. Two have been published in peer reviewed journals.

• *Management/leadership skills* from serving as Secretary of the Benin Medical Students Association (1988-89), co-ordinating junior doctors duty rotas and currently serving on 'Clinical effective committee'.

DUCATION
1992 -1997: University of Benin, Nigeria studying for the MB ChB
- distinctions in Pathology, Biochemistry, Medicine and Public Health
- secretary to Benin University Ballroom Dancing Society

CURRENT APPOINTMENT
Aug.2001-to date: LAT in Infectious Diseases, North Manchester General Hospital, Crumpsall, Manchester
- inpatient and outpatient management of infectious conditions
- middle grade cover for general medicine and care of the elderly
- teaching medical students and senior house officers.

PREVIOUS APPOINTMENTS
Aug 2000- July 2001: *Senior house officer in Medicine*, Manchester Royal Infirmary:
- inpatient and outpatient management of general medical conditions
- middle grade cover for general medicine and care of the elderly
- teaching medical students and senior house officers.

Jan 1999- July 2000: Preparing for and taking PLAB and doing an 8-week clinical attachment in General Medicine in Bradford Royal Infirmary.

Sept 1996- Dec 1998: Registrar in Medicine, Benin University Hospital, Nigeria:
- inpatient and ambulatory general tropical medicine
- teaching medical students and senior house officers
- chairman of the junior doctors' committee; liaising with hospital management
Jan 1994- Aug 1996: Medical officer in the Nigerian Army
- compulsory national service providing medical care in rural areas

Jan - Dec 1993: Pre-registration house officer, Benin University Hospital, Benin.
- 3 months in Paediatrics, Obstetrics and gynaecology, Medicine and Surgery.

RESEARCH

Ischaemic heart disease and income in males in Benin University Hospital (1997). Ischaemic heart disease and myocardial infarction are commoner among affluent males, and less so in females and poorer men.

AUDIT

Adequacy of documentation of recommended antibiotics for mycoplasma infection in discharged patients June 2002. Discharge letters for 100 patients with mycoplasma pneumonia were analysed for information on antibiotics used. 75 named the erythromycin, the dose and frequency; 20 named erythromycin, but gave no dose or frequency; and in 8 only 'antibiotics were given' was found. *A paper based on audit has been submitted to "Journal of Clinical Audit".*

PRESENTATIONS

1. Ischaemic heart disease and income in Benin city males. Annual Meeting of Nigeria Cardiological Association, Abuja, Nigeria, September 1997.

2. Adequacy of documentation of recommended antibiotics for mycoplasma infection in discharged patients. Quarterly Audit Meeting, North Manchester General Hospital. October 2002.

PUBLICATIONS

Chieke E, et. al. Ischaemic heart disease and income in Benin city males. *University Hospital Medical Journal 1998;* 3(4):34-36.

HOBBIES

Ballroom and disco dancing
Listening to Igbo music.

Dr. Ghalib's and Dr. Chieke's curricula vitae anticipate important questions:
- Who is he/she (age, sex, nationality)?
- What does he/she expect to gain from this job?
- What are her/his qualifications, skills and experience?
- Is he/she likely to be an asset to our department?

Dr. Chieke prefers to include the names and addresses of her referees in her Covering Letters. That way she can name different referees for different jobs and specialties.

The two examples above demonstrate how a CV is crafted from the individual's professional history. A more experience doctor's CV is generally longer because he usually has had a more varied experience.

3.7 Quality of printed CV

Your CV should have a neat, attractive layout and printed on good quality white paper with a good printer (inkjet or laser are best). If you do not know how to type, you should learn. There is software to teach you touch-typing from your computer keyboard. If you use a typewriter then you should use a new black ribbon to type your CV.

Quality and weight (thickness) of paper

Hospitals, universities and private business use $80gm/m^2$ paper for their documents. Yet some applicants for SHO jobs print their CVs on thick expensive paper. Recruiters are not influenced by the thickness or cost of the paper, but by what is written on it. There are many varieties of good white $80gm/m^2$ printing paper on the market. It is not necessary to use paper heavier than $100gm/m^2$ for a CV.

3.8 Commercial CV writers

Several companies *produce* CVs. However don't assume that they will *write* a CV for you. They do not know about your education, qualifications, leadership skills, clinical experience, no about your hobbies and interests. You still have to write these out before the company can *type and print* (*produce*) your CV.

They help with layout and printing but only *you can write your CV*. They charge a premium (a lot of money) for editing your writing (cutting out unnecessary or irrelevant detail) and for typing and printing the result. They print the CV on unnecessarily expensive paper and charge you for the privilege!

Do not waste good money paying a private company to write a CV for you. Sorry, if you want a winning CV, you must create it yourself. Write and the edit the document and pay for *typing and printing*. It is cheaper that way.

3.9 What to leave out of CVs

Your CV should present you in the best light. On its strength you will either be selected for interview or rejected. You have full control on how you present yourself in your CV.

No lies or fabrications in CVs

Your CV should be based on the truth. However you should not present yourself in a negative way. You should emphasise your achievements. Lies must be excluded from your CV:

> The GMC Professional Conduct Committee found a doctor guilty of serious professional misconduct after she made false claims about her academic achievements and employment history. The Committee suspended her registration for 12 months (*GMC News 14 October 2002*)

Dr Chieke did not mention that he retook Anatomy and Statistics exams at university. Neither did she apologise for her poor netball skills. She enjoys ballroom dancing and Igbo music. She is happy to talk about either.

In *Managing interviews,* we shall discuss how to talk about past failures, as learning experiences!

3.10 Length of CV

Academic institutions and professional bodies, like medicine, insist on detailed curricula vitae with every job and publications listed. Your CV should give enough details to convey your skills and experience adequately. Its length will depend on the number of jobs you have held, your clinical experience, audits, presentations and publications. Two pages should suffice for a PRHO seeking his first SHO post; while the registrar applying for a consultant post may need several pages.

3.11 Language of your CV

Your CV should be written in an active language. Emphasise your achievements, skills and, contributions to teams you have worked with.

Mind your grammar and spelling. Use a spellchecker (if working with a computer) or your dictionary and then read through the document carefully. Poor spelling and bad grammar whisper to the recruiter.....

"I do not have an English dictionary"
"I can't bother to use a spellchecker"
"Do not trust me to do anything right"
"I am not interested in the job"
"I want to fail."

So, bad spelling and poor grammar invite the recruiter to add your CV to the *'reject'* pile.

Use positive/action words wherever possible. They give the impression of an active, decisive individual. Examples:

achieved	co-ordinated	organised	sampled
analysed	examined	operated	taught
audited	managed	organised	tested **etc.**

3.12 Common errors in CVs
The following are some of the errors commonly found in CVs:
- Too long, too fancy
- Misspellings and/or bad grammar
- Disorganised, too many irregularities
- Badly set out, poorly typed
- Too many obvious omissions
- Out of date or irrelevant details.

3.12.1 Too long
Your CV has one job to do- convey your suitability for a job to the recruiter. It is not the length, but the content that maters. If you follow 'Usual Format for Medical CVs, by the time you have covered all the topics, your CV will be at least 2 typed pages long. If what is needed is in those pages then that is all you should write.

Of course after you have done several jobs and participated in audits, teaching, committee work, research, publishing and clinical governance, your CV will legitimately be long without being too long. It is your duty to write a *clear, concise, precise, and simple* CV.

3.12.2 Too fancy

Word processors and computers have made it too easy to vary the size of letters and their styles (fonts). Some doctors seem to be determined to include as many fonts as possible in their CV. While intended to impress, different letter sizes, fanciful fonts, excessive highlights (bold typefaces) or outlining every heading, result in bizarre documents.

The layout of your CV should make it easy to read and locate information. The CVs for Dr. Ghalib and Dr. Chieke uses one size of letters, one font type (Times New Roman), capitals, bold (**darker**) letters and italics (*slanted letters*) to create documents that are easy to read (so I hope).

3.12.4 Misspellings and/or bad grammar

Your computer spellchecker will not distinguish between *they, their,* and *there*. It will accept *wear, were,* and *ware*; and many other words with similar pronunciations, slightly different spelling, but different meanings. Only you, by reading your CV carefully, can ensure the right word has been used.

There are no shortcuts to good grammar. If you want to improve your grammar, excellent help is available (at a small price):

1 Strunk W, White EB. **The elements of Style.** London: Longman 1999.
2. Jarvie G. **Bloomsbury Grammar Guide.** London: Bloomsbury 2000.

3.12.5 Disorganised, too many irregularities

Your CV should be easy to read. A disorganised and irregular document is often caused by not following recognised formats or established typing conventions, mixing capitals and low case letters in lists or titles, irregular indentation and excess guttering.

Not following recognised formats

Although the information is somewhere in the CV, it is difficult to find. Career plans may be mixed with skills, audit with hobbies, etc.

Not following typing rules

Omitting the usual space between numbers, symbols and words. Example:

23June instead of *23 June*

Number:235 instead of *Number: 235*

Mixing capitals and low case letters

Various combinations of capitals and lower case letters (**W** and **w**, **G** and **g**, **P** and **p,** etc.) may be scattered throughout the CV. This is more obvious in lists and highlighted titles.

Examples:

Summary
- think carefully of what to include or exclude from the CV
- **W**rite a focused, clear, concise and simple CV
- check your spelling and grammar carefully.

Instead of:
- think carefully of what to include or exclude from the CV
- write a focused, clear, concise and simple CV
- check your spelling and grammar carefully.

Or
- Think carefully of what to include or exclude from the CV
- Write a focused, clear, concise and simple CV
- Check your spelling and grammar carefully

---

*July 1997- June 1998: **registrar in general Paediatrics,*** Wigan Infirmary

Instead of:
*July 1997- June 1998: **Registrar in general paediatrics,*** Wigan Infirmary,
or
*July 1997- June 1998: **Registrar in General Paediatrics,*** Wigan Infirmary.

Irregular indentation

Uneven indentation creates misalignment of the text on the left and makes the document shabby. Use the same indent throughout the document.

Excess guttering on the left
> An excessively wide margin (gutter), *as in this paragraph*, pushing the text to the right. What is the gutter for?

Individually these are trivial faults. However if your CV contains several of them, it may fail in its mission. It may not get you an interview with the recruiter.

3.12.6 Too many obvious omissions

I read CVs in which applicants do not list qualifications (not even the MB ChB or BM BS). Often the university awarding the MB BS is not named. State your qualifications, name the source of your degrees. Other applicants will do so. Why would you disadvantage yourself?

Missing months and years
While a few weeks may not matter, gaps of several months or years will be noted. Unexplained gaps invite speculations. *Was he sick, studying for exams, in prison...?* Mind the gaps! Account for significant gaps in your work history.

3.12.7 Hiding experience acquired abroad

I recall reading a CV in which it was not clear what the applicant had done over a period of 12 months. It turned out that he was in his national army on national service (working as a doctor!). Why was he ashamed of it?

Later I learnt he had been advised to minimise or hide experience gained abroad. Over the years I found that talking about my experience abroad is easy and rewarding. Many interviews like it- some took over the talking!

Some applicants minimise (almost hide) experience gain abroad. Perhaps they believe that it is not relevant to their future in the NHS. That is wrong. It is relevant and should be described properly. Interviewers want to know what you did before coming to the UK. Tell them in your CV.

Describe your experience abroad clearly and concisely. Explain unusual titles (name British equivalents). Employers want to know what you did in the time between graduation and coming to the UK.

3.12.8 Out of date details
One SHO working in obstetrics and gynaecology submitted a CV in an application for a paediatrics job. The Career Plan stated: "after finishing house jobs I would like to work in Obstetrics and Gynaecology to gain accreditation for Family Planning". The doctor had not revised the CV prepared towards the end of the PRHO year before applying for the paediatrics post.

This error did not stop him from being short-listed, but if it were accompanied by others, it could lead to rejection. Therefore:
- keep your CV up to date; revise it before posting
- give all relevant information in a pleasing format
- ensure there are no unexplained gaps
- check the spelling and grammar.

3.13 New CV for new application?
Yes, ideally. However for most PRHO or SHO jobs, a good CV, revised before the next round of applications is enough. But you should write a new 'Covering Letter' for each application (*See 5.7: The covering letter*). Senior doctors (specialist registrars, associate specialist, consultants or GP principal) should rewrite their CVs for each application. Or rather recast the CV to address the person descriptions of the post they seek.

Keep your CV up to-date
Update your CV each time there is a significant change in your career or you achieve something important (change jobs, complete and present an audit, publish a paper or take on new clinical or leadership responsibilities).

When needed, rewriting the CV will be easy. All the information will be there waiting to be arranged according to the needs of the position sought.

Many capable applicants have missed good positions because their CVs were untidy or plainly irrelevant. Does your CV convey your skills and capabilities, work record and achievements concisely and clearly? If not, revise and rewrite it till it does.

3.14 Sending your CV to a recruiter

Avoid sending your CV by e-mail or fax. The quality of the printer and/ or paper used by the recipient may not be good. What the recruiter sees may be a poor version of your document. This could ruin the impression you worked so hard to create. If the computer formats are incompatible your document may be rendered unintelligible.

If you must send the document by e-mail then send it as an attachment to the e-mail. Include a covering letter in the attachment too. Immediately send a printed copy by normal post. Sure, it is overkill!

Summary

- The job of a CV is to get you an interview with the employer/recruiter.

- Think carefully about what to include or exclude from the CV. No lies. However you should not volunteer unfavourable facts.

- Write a focused, clear, concise and simple CV. It should be well presented and easy to read. Untidy, poorly prepared CVs are rejected.

- Read the person specifications carefully and ensure your CV conveys the qualifications and experience required.

- Ensure your qualifications and clinical experience are easy to find. Give dates, job title, name of employer and summarise your responsibilities.
- Give concise details of teaching experience, clinical audit, research, courses attended, and management and leadership skills.

- Describe experience gained abroad fully. Give British equivalents of unusual job titles.

- Describe postgraduate qualification gained abroad. List the title of the dissertation or thesis for your MS, MD or other degree. Describe research done abroad. List your publications.

- Choose your referees carefully and get their permission before citing them as referees. Do not use people likely to give you a bad reference (unless you don't want the job!).

- Briefly describe your non-professional interests outside medicine. Present yourself as a competent, skilled worker with a normal life.

- Be prepared to discuss and clarify statements made in your CV. Do not include anything you are not happy to discuss at interview.
- Keep a copy of the CV you submit in application. You should have it to read before the interview (if shortlisted!).

Update your CV regularly- you may need it sooner!

Further Reading

1. Eggert M. **The Perfect CV.** Arrow Business Books 1999.

2. Hutton-Taylor S. **Marketing yourself as an overseas doctor**. *BMJ* 2002; 324: s75

3. GMC. Case Book: **Doctor suspended after making false claims.** GMC News 14 October 2002. www.gmc-uk.org

---

4. Clinical attachments

4.1 What is a clinical attachment?
A clinical attachment is the association of a novice clinician (junior doctor) with an experienced clinician (a consultant) to introduce the novice to a clinical discipline or environment. Most foreign doctors find the NHS strange and difficult to understand. They need a guide through the mystery of the NHS and reassurance that their clinical knowledge and skills are sound. A clinical attachment meets these needs too.

4.2 Do you need a clinical attachment?
Yes you do. Passing PLAB will have reaffirmed your faith in your clinical knowledge and skills. However, it will not have taught you how your knowledge and skills are used in the NHS, no how to navigate the language and culture of British medicine.

The GMC states that during induction periods, (a clinical attachment is indeed an induction) overseas doctors should be provided with:

---

a. Orientation to the local living and working environment, including the culture and expectations of the patients that they will be helping to treat and the colleagues with whom they will be working.

b. Opportunities to develop their communication skills.

c. An introduction to the principles of professional practice set out by the GMC in *'Good Medical Practice'*.

You need a period of clinical attachment to:
• meet and shadow doctors (usually senior house officers) working at the level you expect to work

• study health care culture and the relationships between different health care professionals.

- enable you to meet and get to know NHS consultants from whom you may later seek job references

- enable you to refresh your medical knowledge and clinical skills before embarking on full time work in the NHS.

4.3 Finding clinical attachments

There is no central organisation that arranges clinical attachments for doctors. Although in the 1970s the GMC did organise clinical attachments for foreign doctors coming into the NHS, it no longer does.

You can arrange a clinical attachment on your own by writing to a hospital consultant or to a hospital medical staffing officer.

4.3.1 Where do you find consultants' names?
Dr Foster's Guide to Healthcare Services in UK
Telephone 0906 190021 **www.drfoster.co.uk**

4.3.2 Royal medical colleges
Each year UK royal medical colleges publish handbooks with names and addresses of their members and fellows. Copies of these handbooks may be found in public libraries.

Postal addresses, telephone numbers and websites of the royal medical colleges are listed below:

The Royal College of Anaesthetists
48/49 Russell Square, London WC1B 4JP
Telephone 0207 813 1900 www.rcoa.ac.uk

Royal College of General Practitioners
14 Princes Gate, Hyde Park, London Sw7 1PU
Telephone 0207 581 3232 www.rcgp.org.uk

The Royal College of Obstetricians and Gynaecologists
27 Sussex Place, Regents Park, London NW1 4RG
Telephone 0207 402 2317 www.rcog.org.uk

The Royal College of Ophthalmologists
17 Cornwall Terrace, London NW1 4QW
Telephone 0207 935 0702 www.rcophth.ac.uk

The Royal College of Paediatrics and Child Health
50 Hallam Street, London W1N 6DE
Telephone 0207 307 5600 www.rcpch.ac.uk

The Royal College of Pathologists
2 Carlton House Terrace, London SW1Y 5AF
Telephone 0207 930 5861 www.rcpath.org

The Royal College of Physicians of Edinburgh
9 Queen Street, Edinburgh EH2 1JQ
Telephone 0131 225 7324 www.rcpe.ac.uk

The Royal College of Physicians and Surgeon of Glasgow
234-242 St Vincent Street, Glasgow G2 5RJ
Telephone 0141 221 6072 www.rcpsglasgow.ac.uk

The Royal College of Physicians of London
11 St Andrews Place, Regents Park, London NW1 4LE
Telephone 0207 935 1174 www.rcplondon.ac.uk

The Royal College of Surgeons of Edinburgh
Nicolson Street, Edinburgh EH8 9DW
Telephone 0131 527 1600 www.rcsed.ac.uk

The Royal College of Surgeon of England
35-43 Lincoln's Inn Fields, London WC2A 3PN
Telephone 0207 405 3474 www.rcseng.ac.uk

The Royal College of Psychiatrists
17 Belgrave Square, London SW1X 8PG
Telephone 0207 235 2351 www.rcpsych.ac.uk

The Royal College of Radiologists
38 Portland Place, London W1N 3DG
Telephone 0207 636 4462 www.rcr.ac.uk

Write to a hospital consultant requesting to spend several weeks on a clinical attachment in her/his department.

4.3.3 Write to a hospital consultant

Dr Sanjit Kumar
415 Seymour Grove
Old Trafford M16 0LW

Tel. 077 9745x4 (mobile)

12 June 2002

Mr Yousuf Kasule
Consultant Neurosurgeon
Hope Hospital
Stott Lane
Salford M6 8HD

Dear Mr Kasule

Re: Request for a clinical attachment in Neurosurgery
I would be grateful if you could enable me to spend 8 weeks on a clinical attachment in your department at Hope Hospital. This would enable me to observe and gain an insight into the working of the NHS.

I am a 30 year old surgeon with an MS in Surgery from Madras University, India. I have passed part 1 of PLAB and will sit the final in two months.

The details of my education, work experience and referees are shown in the enclosed curriculum vitae.

Yours sincerely

S Kumar
Sanjit Kumar MB MS

The consultant may offer you an attachment and ask you to sort out administrative details with the medical staffing office.

Write to a few consultants at a time, wait a few weeks before writing again. If you are unable to take up an offer, write back, thank the consultant and explain why you will not be taking up the offer.

4.3.4 Writing to a hospital
You can write to the hospital's medical staffing officer and ask her to find you a clinical attachment in the hospital. If the hospital offers clinical attachments, she will contact a consultant in the specialty of your interest. If a consultant agrees to supervise you, the medical staffing officer will then tell you how to sort out administrative details.

4.4 Benefiting from clinical attachments
You should use your time on a clinical attachment as effectively as possible.

Get to know your host consultant- the doctor who offered to supervise your clinical attachment. Attend his/her clinics, ward rounds, operating sessions and teaching activities. Keep in touch with your host. By offering you a clinical attachment he/she is willing to act as your referee.

Shadow the doctor whose job you would do if you were employed in that hospital in four weeks' time. Spend most of the attachment shadowing, and where acceptable, assisting the PHRH, the SHO or registrar. Shadow her/him on ward rounds, A & E work, admissions ward, on call duties, collecting and processing laboratory samples, educational activities - all legitimate hospital activities the doctor engages in.

Karim was excited at securing a clinical attachment to Prof. Ward, clinical professor of paediatrics at a famous university. He followed the professor to clinics, ward rounds and teaching sessions. At other times he went to the library or watched TV in the doctor's mess.

He did not shadow SHOs to delivery rooms, neonatal resuscitation, the neonatal unit no did he attend SHO/registrar ward rounds. He did not attend any activities that did not involve consultants or professors. After passing part 2 PLAB, he obtained a job as SHO at a district general hospital. He did not know how to manage SHO duties. Registrars spent more time showing him what to do than any other SHO.

The registrars recognised that he was quite a good clinician. However by the end of the appointment, his consultant was still under the impression that Karim was a poor doctor. She would not give him a good reference.

Observe the functions of various clinical and managerial staff
The NHS employs a wide range of cadres- administrative, clinical and managerial. You should try to gain an appreciation of their roles.

Appreciate clinical governance and risk management. Although these may not appear to be your primary concern, it is wise to observe the attitudes and responses of your consultants and registrars to issues related to clinical governance and risk management. Clinical governance touches all people who directly or indirectly work with or for patients.

Contribute to clinical discussions on ward rounds, outpatient clinics and teaching sessions. Your hosts will be happy to learn from you as you learn from them. Your host consultant will have the opportunity to appreciate your knowledge and reasoning skills.

Summary
- Write to a hospital consultant requesting a clinical attachment in her/his department

- Give your host consultant the opportunity to know you so that he/she can appreciate your medical knowledge and clinical skills

- Spend most of the attachment shadowing doctors whose job you would be doing if you were working at the hospital in 4 weeks' time

- Observe and study the language of health care, human relationships and the functions of various health care cadres.

Further Reading

1. Hutton-Taylor S. **Marketing yourself as an overseas doctor**.
    BMJ 2002; 324: S75.

2. Scoote M, Thaventhiran J, Elkington A. **Progress towards higher specialist training**. *BMJ* 2002; 325: s49.

3. Berlin A, Cheeroth S. **Clinical attachments for overseas doctors**.
    BMJ 2002; 325: s160- s161.

4. Swierczynski M. **Induction courses for international doctors**.
    BMJ 2002; 325: s159.

5. Applying for jobs

5.1 Which specialty?

Now that you have passed PLAB how will you decide on the medical specialty to pursue? Will it be surgical, medical or laboratory medicine, general practice or other community based activity? Do you enjoy all specialties and continue to drift from one post to another? What factors should you consider when choosing a specialty?

5.1.1 What do you want from your career?

Think about what you want to gain from your career before seeking advice from others:
- Why did you study medicine?
- What would be your ideal specialty?
- Do you like working with your hands, discussing things or both?
- Do you like working with groups, interacting with different people?
- Are there factors that would make some specialties unsuitable?
- Do you/would you have access to training and clinical experience?
- What qualifications and experience do you need for the specialty?
- Are you free (of dependants' needs) to pursue your ideal specialty?

5.1.2 What do you enjoy?

This is the most important factor. Do not be persuaded, seduced into a specialty that you do not enjoy. You need to mix the hard work of medical practice with enthusiasm and fun. At the end of the day/shift/night on-call you should feel that you have given a useful service to those who needed your help and enjoyed your work.

While some doctors thrive on stress, others prefer quieter work-lives. Although most doctors enjoy contact with patients, some prefer the challenges of laboratory medicine, medical research or public health. Whatever you inclination you need to choose your specialty carefully. Changing course after several years in specialty X is painful and is viewed suspiciously by employers.

When choosing a medical specialty an advisor may help you to:
- Obtain information on specialty requirements and job prospects

- Ascertain your personal suitability for a specialty
- Clarify advantages and disadvantages of different specialties
- Decide between hospital medicine or general practice
- Pick a particular specialty or subspecialty
- Explore career options outside medicine.

5.1.3 Career prospects

For many reasons, some specialties are easier to enter than others. Job prospects are difficult to predict and the popularity of disciplines varies from time to time almost randomly. Be realistic about opportunities in competitive specialties, about your qualifications compared with those of the competition.

At the moment (2003), competition for registrar jobs is harshest in surgery, general medicine and paediatrics. There is a shortage of consultants in psychiatry, histopathology, anaesthesia and radiology. But SHO posts are scarce in A & E, Anaesthesia and histopathology.

The situation changes and you should keep an eye on the demand and supply of SpR, GP registrar as well as consultant and GP principal posts as appropriate for you. Do not get so fixated on one subspecialty that you wouldn't consider openings in other disciplines.

Foreign doctors have traditionally been welcomed into the less popular disciplines. In the 1970 and 1980s, these were general practice, pathology, geriatrics, community child health and family planning. The picture however is changing. Many of the community services (child health and family planning) are integrating into hospital specialties or primary care trusts (PCTs). Keep yourself informed.

5.1.4 Find an adviser

It may be beneficial to speak to somebody you already known so that the advice can be tailored to your personal circumstances. However, a new adviser may be more impartial. If you have narrowed you choice of specialty to a few, find an adviser from each of those specialties. He/she will have the knowledge and experience to give you detailed advice.

Ask colleagues about individuals from whom they have received impartial and valuable advice.

5.1.5 What do you know about the following disciplines?

Accident and emergency medicine
Anaesthesia and pain control
General practice
Medicine, geriatrics and subspecialties
  Cardiology
  Chest medicine
  Dermatology
  Endocrinology
  Gastroenterology
  Genito-urinary medicine
  Nephrology
  Neurology
  Rheumatology
Obstetrics, gynaecology + subspecialties
Paediatrics, community child health and
  subspecialties
Psychiatry + sub-specialties
  Child and adolescent psychiatry
  Learning disability
  Psychogeriatrics
  Forensic psychiatry
  Psychoanalysis
Radiology and its sub-specialties
  Roentgenography (X-rays images)
  Ultrasonography
  CT, MRI scanning
  Intervention radiology
Surgery + its sub-specialties

Audiological medicine
Academic medicine
Armed forces
Clinical pharmacology
Clinical neurophysiology
Environmental health
Health service management
Medical advisor (public, private)
Medical computing (informatics)
Medical journalism
Medical politics
Occupational medicine
Ophthalmology
Palliative care
Pathology and its subspecialties
  Medical microbiology
  Clinical genetics
  Chemical pathology
  Clinical haematology
  Clinical immunology
  Blood transfusion
  Forensic pathology
  Histopathology
  Immunology
Pharmaceutical medicine
Police surgeon/prison doctor
Public health medicine
Sports medicine
Etcetera, etc.

Inform your adviser of your career aims, achievements to date, perceived weaknesses and strengths. State the specific nature of the advice you seek before the meeting. This will allow her/him to look into relevant issues or to refer you to a more appropriate person.

Arrange not to be bleeped or telephoned during the meeting. Be as clear and concise about the help you seek, the choices you have already made and the specialties you do not wish to pursue. Write down important suggestions so that you can reflect on them later.

It is often difficult to decide whether to follow advice or not. Do not reject unpalatable advice out of hand. Ask yourself if the advisor could be right. Did he/she give reasons for the advice? Does it fit personal circumstances? Does it agree with advice from others, including those who are already following the proposed career path? After you have made you choice, thank the advisor for meeting you and inform her/him how useful the meeting was.

5.1.6 Variety, excitement and tedium
Medical practice means seeing patients with the same conditions over and over, repeating procedures regularly and giving the same or similar explanations repeatedly. It is not like medical school where learning new things is the norm. Graduation gave you an entry ticket into the world of unavoidable tedium and repetition. That is why your choice is important- to enable you to enjoy the tedium and repetition.

I remember, as an SHO in Medicine, working with Mark, a PRHO. He was bright, clever and ambitious. He knew more syndromes than I did. However there were no opportunity to study the syndromes beyond clerking patient after patient and collecting blood sample after blood sample. The tedium got him. He lost interest and left in his 3rd month of medical practice.

Some specialities have more variety than others. Accident and emergency medicine is possibly the least predictable. However some doctors want something less exciting than A & E. The choice is wide in hospital medical, surgical, laboratory, managerial and community medicine.

5.1.7 Getting further advice
Advice on medical specialism is available from the royal colleges and their faculties, postgraduate deans, postgraduate tutors, regional advisors, and college advisors. If you are not familiar with these organisations or officers, ask you senior colleagues, the medical librarian or your clinical tutor.

The best advice, probably, will come from those who are already established in the specialties you are considering. Many of them will be happy to discuss the advantages and disadvantages of their posts. They may also direct you to the more appropriate sources of information.

Your choice will make the difference between 30 years of enjoyment and 30 years of drudgery. Think carefully before you decide.

5.2 At what level?

Doctors who have passed PLAB find it difficult to decide the level at which to seek employment in the NHS. It is unlikely that a consultant from a non-European Union or North American country will find work in the NHS at the same level, unless he has EU qualifications- hence he would not need PLAB!

Has he worked in the UK before?

After PLAB most doctors find work as senior house officers or pre-registration house officers, initially. Doctors who have done PRHO jobs in the UK may get SHO jobs ahead of those who have not. Recruiters want to know if the doctor has *"worked in the UK before."*

5.3 Finding medical jobs

In the UK, most medical jobs are advertised in *BMJ Careers* and on **www.bmj.com.** Medical jobs also appear on the following websites:

The British Medical Journal	www.bmj.com
The Lancet Interactive	www.thelancet.com/
Health Recruitment	www.heath.co.uk/
Direct Medical Appointments	www.directmedical.co.uk/
Jobs in Medicine	www.jobsin.co.uk/health/ire.htm
BioMedNet	www.bmn.com/
Doctor Job (GTI Careerscope)	www.doctorjob.co.uk/
PersonnelNet Health	www.personnelnet.co.uk/
Doctors4UK	www.doctor4uk.com/NHS
Professionals	www.nhsprofessionals.nhs.uk/

5.3.1 Locum agencies

Locum agencies help doctors find temporary work. They usually charge the employer (hospital) a fee for the service. You are paid more for accepting a locum job through a locum agency than taking it directly from the hospital's medical staffing department. I do not understand the economics. I gave up trying to understand the logic either!

5.3.2 Networking/ word of mouth
Friends or other contacts may have information about jobs. Ask them to tell you of interesting jobs they hear about. Develop a network (linked groups) of individuals who will tell you of coming openings. This is called *networking*

5.4 Should you apply?
Let us assume you are looking for a PRHO or SHO job- the level at which most doctors who have passed PLAB enter the NHS. *You have found some interesting jobs in 'BMJ Careers':*

• What should you do next? *Contact the hospital for job descriptions. You have read the job descriptions. Do you meet the specifications?*

• You have the qualifications. Do want to apply for any of them?

Study the job description
• What would your duties be if you got the job?
• Are your skills adequate for the job?

When you apply for a job, the question asked about you is -*Is he/she the right doctor for the job?* Will she make a good house officer? Will she do the job willingly? Will she fit into the clinical team?

Look at your qualifications and skills
• Are they relevant to the post?
• Are you aiming too high or too low?

Before applying for a job, ensure that you like the post and hospital. Read the job description and person specification again.

Talk to the doctor doing the advertised job
- How good is the hospital?
- Are the nurses and consultants friendly?
- What is good and not so good about the job?
- Does the department encourage studying for exams?

Now you are in a position to *decide about making the application.* How shall you convince them that you are the right candidate?

Send them your best CV and Covering Letter; or carefully complete their application form. Ensure that your application works for you. Provide them with evidence that you are the answer to their needs. Help them conclude that: *"This is the right doctor."*

5.5 The covering letter
For registrar and more senior positions, the covering letter is almost as important as the CV or application form. The covering letter:
- introduces your CV or application from to the recruiter
- highlighting the candidates suitability for the posts
- entices the recruiter to read the CV.

The covering should be *clear, concise, precise,* and *simple.* It should be typed. Its layout should make it easy for important details to be noticed.

5.5.1 *Write to a named individual or officer* responsible for recruiting.
Find out the officer's name, title and full address. Follow the structure of letters discussed in chapter 2 and provide your contact details so that the recruiter can contact you either by post, telephone/fax or e-mail.

5.5.2 *Name the post and quote its reference number*
This ensures that the application goes to the right office and right desk. The hospital may be recruiting for different jobs of the same grade.

5.5.3 *State concisely why you are the right doctor for the post*
Briefly highlight your qualifications, clinical experience and achievements, and important non-clinical attributes (research, clinical audit, teaching, leadership and management, languages spoke, computer and IT skills and others).

17 Campion Close
Eccleshall
Stafford ST21 6SR
Tel: 077 374x44 (mobile)
echieke@yahoo.co.uk

12 October 2002

Miss Patricia Matthews
Catsford Deanery
Catsford House
Catsford M76 5PQ

Dear Miss Matthews

Re: Application for SpR post in Infectious Diseases, Ref. C213
May I apply for the advertised post of Specialist Registrar in Infectious
Diseases. I have the experience to perform the duties and learn from the post:

General medical experience in tropical medicine, infectious diseases and
hospital medical subspecialties.

Teaching and training skills come from teaching medical students and
senior house officers using didactic and problem based learning methods.

Research and audit experience has come from audits and research studies
done and presented locally and/or at regional meetings.

Leadership skills came from serving as secretary of Benin University
Students Association, and currently on the department's 'Clinical
Effectiveness' and 'Clinical Governance' committees.

A copy of my curriculum vitae is enclosed.

Yours sincerely,
EChieke
Ebele Chieke MB ChB MRCP

End with *'Yours sincerely'* (if you used the officer name at the beginning of the letter) or *'Yours faithfully'* (if an official title only was used). Sign the letter and print your name bellow the signature.

5.5.4 Examples of Covering Letters
- Seeking a clinical attachment *(page 27, 56)*
- Applying for a PRHO post *(page 28)*
- Applying for an SHO post *(page 29)*
- Applying for an SpR post *(page 68)*

5.6 Application forms
Some hospitals (trusts) insist on candidates completing application forms). Obtain and complete the form carefully. It is best to use black ink. If your handwriting is poor, then write in clear CAPITALS. Be careful with capital letters- they can look untidy and may be difficult to read. Answer all the questions even if it means writing *'**No, Nil,** or **Not applicable**'* many times.

Organise your information before completing the form. Your CV should contain sorted information, ready to be transferred to the form. You could practice on a photocopy of the form before completing the original.

If asked to send an application letter in your handwriting, make sure you are able to write neatly (pen, mood, lighting, furniture and posture). Have you heard about character analysis from handwriting? This is said to occur in business recruitment, but not in the NHS- not yet.

5.7 Is a letter good enough?
If asked to apply in writing, you should send your best CV and a typed covering letter written specifically to address the job and person specifications (*the qualifications, experience and skills the ideal candidate would have*) for the post. An ordinary letter is not enough.

Dr Ngaka's application *(page 69)* does not anticipate basic questions:
- What are his qualifications?
- How long has he worked in psychiatry?
- Does he have any hobbies?
- Who are his referees?

Dr Ngaka wrote to a London psychiatrist requesting an SHO post

Dr James Ngaka
PO Box 456
Maseru 100
Lesotho.

5 September 2002

Dr Paul Orchard
Maudsley Hospital
Denmark Hill
London SE5 8AZ

Dear Dr Orchard

Re: Application for a training post in psychiatry
I wish to apply for a training post in psychiatry in your hospital I am a
31year old graduate of the University of Cape Town. I am a medical
officer in psychiatry at Queen Elizabeth II Hospital, Maseru.

Thank you for helping me find a training post in psychiatry.

Yours faithfully,

JNgaka
James Ngaka MB ChB

He could have volunteered answers to these and other questions by
enclosing a copy of his CV with his letter. In a CV you can give a detailed
summary of your career- listing information that would make a letter rather
long and boring. What looks right and proper in a CV may look out of
place in a letter.

Application by CV and covering letter is the standard practice. If an
application form is provided, it should be escorted back by a covering
letter.

5.8 Do they want a CV?

If asked to send a CV, send a clean, current CV. Do you have a current well-composed, typed CV? If not then read '*Writing your CV*'. If your CV is out of date, revise it. Different aspects of your experience, skills and qualifications may need stressing.

Alone, the CV is not enough. It should be escorted by a focused covering letter. The letter should address the person specifications one by one and show that you meet them very well.

5.9 Submitting your CV

Avoid sending your CV by e-mail or fax. The quality of printer and paper used may not be impressive. The version of your CV seen by the recruiter may be a poor version of the original document. This could ruin the impression you worked so hard to create. If the format of your document is incompatible with the recruiter's computers, the pages received could be unintelligible.

If you must, send the document by e-mail. Include the covering letter in the attachment. Send a printed copy by normal post too (of course with covering letter).

Send a copy of your CV to your referees to remind them of who you are and of your good work under their supervision. Junior doctors come and go every six months. Some senior doctors need reminding of who you are, when you worked with them and the highlights of your stay with them. It might also be useful to tell them which job(s) you are applying for.

5.10 Testimonials

Testimonials are commendations written by referees that a candidate keeps with him and may send off with a CV or a completed application form.

Testimonials are less influential than confidential references. Generally UK hospitals do not accept testimonials as references. They prefer to contact your referees confidentially. Naturally nobody sends out a bad testimonial!

5.11 References

References are often obtained by telephone or fax. So ensure that you have included your referee's telephone and fax numbers. This enables the recruiter to get your reference quickly (in minutes rather than days). Please get permission before naming individuals as your referees.

Summary

- Written applications may be made by either:
  - a relevant, neat, typed CV and a Covering Letter; **or**
  - a completed application form and a Covering Letter.

- Sometimes a completed application form *and* a CV are requested. You should send a Covering Letter too.

- Send copies of your CV to your referees to remind them of who you are and of your good work under their supervision.

- Send your application early. It must arrive before the closing date.

Do not send the originals of your documents unless specifically asked. Your prized certificate could get lost. You will take them with you if called for interview.

Further reading

1. Hutton-Taylor S. Marketing yourself as an overseas doctor. *BMJ* 2002; 324: s75

2. Beatty R. **The perfect Cover Letter**. New York: Wiley 1997.

3   Burnet S. **How to get shortlisted.** *BMJ* 2002; 324: s3

4   Bapat S. **The first job.** *BMJ* 2002; 325: S169.

5   Spillane M. **Branding Yourself:** how to look, sound and behave your way to success. Pan Macmillan: London 2000

6. Managing Interviews

6.1 What is an interview?

An interview is the occasion when two parties (individuals or groups) meet and view each other. In job searches this is when applicants (interviewee) are seen (viewed) and questioned by interviewer(s) to determine their suitability for the jobs they seek.

An interview is the opportunity for a doctor to meet and talk with persons (consultants or principal GPs) with jobs to give away. The doctor's aim is to convince interviewers that she is the best there is and so they should give her the job and not someone else.

6.2 What are interviews for?

Several applicants, who meet the person specifications, are short-listed and interviewed to select the most suitable. All applicants interviewed have the technical qualification to do the job.

What needs to be decided is: "*Will he do the job? Will he fit in?*" A sole applicant would not be appointed if he was not suitable for the post.

Interviewers must answer one question: *Is this candidate suitable?*
- *Can this doctor do the job?* All doctors called for interview have the technical qualifications and should be able to do the job.

- *Will she do the job?* Is she willing to meet the needs of the job? If a doctor creates the impression that although capable, she could refuse to do the job, she will not get appointed.

- *Will she fit in?* People want somebody who will fit in nicely.

A candidate may have the diplomas and years of experience but still be unsuitable for a post (because of personality, demeanour, timidity, etc.).

Is he the right person for the job?
Does he have the right qualifications, experience, skills and personality?

Is this the right job for his qualifications and skills? Sometimes an applicant may not get the job because interviewer thinks he would be better employed in a different capacity.

6.3 Pre-interview enquiries and visits

Candidates for senior jobs- specialist registrar, consultant and GP principal are expected to visit the hospital or practice before they apply for the post, and often before interview. Candidates for PRHO and SHO jobs are not normally expected to, but are welcome to visit.

They should telephone and speak with the doctor doing the job who will be able to tell them what doing the job means. He/she may also tell them about the staff (nurses, consultants, registrars and others).

If you visit, you should:
• Look over as much of the hospital as possible (wards, library, doctor on-call rooms, doctors' mess, restaurant, etc.)

• Speak to doctors doing the job you have applied for. Is it educational, enjoyable, exhausting? Ask searching questions and listen to the answers. Discuss the duties; what will the employer expect of you?

• Speak to nurses and consultants about the post and related issues. Are they welcoming? You will work with them if you get the job!

This is the time for you to satisfy yourself that you like the place, that you like the people and the job and understand what is expected of you.

6.4 Preparing for interview

Before the interview, find out as much as possible about the post, the hospital and the department you would be working in:
• Is the hospital friendly?
• Is the department friendly?
• What is it like to work there?
• What are the teaching arrangements?
• Does the hospital welcome foreigners?
• Do the consultants encourage taking exams?

Are you ready to talk about your education, work history, skills and hobbies smoothly and confidently? It would be a shame if you did not remember the contents of your CV. Read the job and person specification again to ensure that your answers are relevant. Do you really want this job?

Before the interview reread a copy of the CV you sent when you applied for the job or used to complete the application form. Your interviewers will have copies of your CV or completed application form in front of them as they question you and may question you about its contents.

Let us list a few questions commonly asked at interviews. How would you answer them?

Job Interviews
- Why did you apply for this job?
- Have you applied for other jobs?
- What are your career objectives?
- What are your main weaknesses?
- What are your main strengths?

Topical issues
You are unlikely to face questions on topical medical, social and political debates of the day at interviews for SHO posts. However expect some at interviews for more senior posts.

Nuclear weapons and test tube babies were once topical. How would respond to a question like *"What do you think about...Tell me about... What are your views on...*
- primary care trusts and health care commissioning?
- community care and hospital bed blocking
- clinical governance and risk management?
- continuous professional development?
- appraisal, assessment and revalidation?
- the private finance initiative?

Not a lot, maybe. But it is worth your effort knowing about such issues. Medicine is practised in an environment ruled/influenced by social and political issues. Politicians determine administrative structures and the funding of health care.

Do you have any questions?

Sometimes interviewers ask if the applicant has any questions. Do you have questions about training, study leave, teaching? Do not ask irrelevant questions. You do not have to ask questions. Thank the panel for the opportunity. Tell them you have talked with doctors and nurses in the department and that they have answered your questions.

6.5 Presenting for interview

You are mentally ready. You have your certificates, identity papers and the invitation to the interview. What have you forgotten?

What will you *look* like *(appearance, confidence and personality);* **sound** like *(voice, language, knowledge and confidence of voice)?*

Often critical decisions (*Yes- no, Trust- Distrust, Love- Hate, Good- Bad,* etc.) are made after brief encounters (interviews). You meet him and in a few moments, you dislike him. He has failed the interview!

Normally only applicants with the right qualifications are invited for interview. So it is not lack of qualifications but rather the ***impression*** you create- your ***appearance, speech, confidence*** and ***personality*** that decides whether you get the job or not. Create a good impression and you may get the job. *Interviews* are *won* or *lost* on *impressions.*

6.5.1 Personal papers

Take your certificates, Identification, GMC registration or legibility for registration, Hepatitis B immune status and other relevant documents with you. If you are successful, the medical staffing officer will want to check them.

6.5.2 Appearance

Your appearance will contribute to your performance at the interview. You should wear smart, clean and socially appropriate clothes. These should be items you are comfortable in- clothes you have worn before, that complement your body and look good (neat, washed and pressed).

Do not wear clothes that make you uncomfortable. If you are uncomfortable you will fidget and give a poor impression.

I usually wear my best and most comfortable trousers, shirt, jacket and shoes. I talk better if I am not being strangled by a tight collar, squeezed by a jacket too small for my chest or a pair of trousers that threatens to split into two each time I shift my buttocks.

Wear clothes that suit the position you seek. Think of the age and potential biases of your interviewers. Wear clothes that are unlikely to offend their sense of propriety. Some fashions are more acceptable than others irrespective of quality (and cost).

A standard shirt is more acceptable that a T-shirt. Jeans (denim) are unacceptable; wear standard trousers. Females tend to wear skirts and browses; however trousers are now more or less acceptable. Business suits are acceptable for women in management or senior clinical positions. It is safer to wear little or no jewellery than to carry excess heavy metal!

It is difficult to predict what will annoy an interviewer. Senior doctors are more conservative than the general public. It may be safer to be a little conservative too. If you look young for you age, adopt the fashions of those 5 or so years older. Dress for a serious professional interview and not for a young people's party.

Is your *hair groomed, fingernails trimmed and clean. Are your shoes in good repair and shined?* Have you bathed? It would be a shame if you offended the interviewer's nose. Better not to smoke before the interview.

I know very little about perfumes. A candidate who smelled like a perfume factory would not impress many interviewers. Use light perfume; and only if you normally use the stuff and know what is good and what is not.

6.5.3 Politeness
On arrival at the place of interview, speak and make your inquiries politely. You never know who is looking and listening. Do not offend any body. You could meet them again in the interview room! Bosses do not have to be behind big desks before they start interviewing you (*watching, listening and talking to you*). Remain alert and polite till your interview is finished and you have left the hospital.

When you enter the interview room wait till asked to sit. Then sit right into the chair with you back supported by back of the chair. Adjust your position if necessary till you are comfortable. Do not sit on the edge and risk falling off. Sit up, and remain attentive. Look at each member of the panel as he/she is introduced to you.

6.5.4 Behaving during the interview
- Do not draw attention to your weaknesses
- Do not criticise your previous employer
- Do not smoke, even if invited to
- Do not interrupt the interviewer
- Do not argue with the interviewer
- Do not get too familiar or personal
- Smile; it is allowed, laugh appropriately
- Do tell the truth; it is easier to talk about
- Speak clearly, succinctly, give full answers.

6.5.5 Confidence and Personality
Your confidence and personality will be judged from your grooming, dress, composure, mannerisms, and speech. Your confidence is improved by how well you have prepared for the interview. You portray your best personality if you are well dressed, polite, speak clearly and audibly and knowledgeably.

6.5.6 Body language
Avoid annoying mannerisms (picking your nose, yawning, clicking your knuckles, constantly clearing your throat, etc). Do not give the impression that you do not care about the outcome of the interview. Keep an interested and alert face.

6.5.7 Speech
We speak to convey information, to be understood. So when you answer questions, *speak so that your answer is heard clearly and understood.* You should neither whisper nor shout.

Watch the interviewers to see if they hear and understand your answers. Your purpose is to convince them to give the job to you. If they cannot hear you well, they will not know how good you are. Look at each interviewer eye-to-eye for brief moments. Move your attention to the person speaking to you and listen. Understand the question before answering it. If it is not clear, ask him or her to explain it. *Speak clearly, concisely, and simply.*

Do not use jargon or abbreviations unless you are certain your interviewers know them too. Use ordinary words and language. Answer the question asked. Be *clear, brief* and *informative* in your answers. Give your answers politely and confidently. If you don't know say so clearly and confidently.

If an interviewer is talking do not interrupt. Let him talk. Listen and be ready to answer the question that will follow the speech.

6.6 Questions about past experience
Sometimes candidates are asked about past failures. Be prepared to talk about something that did not turnout well. Talk about failures whose cause was identified, lessons learnt and which you are now able to discuss calmly and rationally. Stress the lessons and not the failures. Give one example only. You do not want to dwell on failure.

Other questions asked at medical interviews
- Tell us about an interesting case you have dealt with recently
- What is the most challenging clinical situation you have dealt with?
- Tell me about your last audit (or research project).

How would you answer them?

Summary
- Is it the right job, should you apply for the job?
- Send your best CV and a covering letter?
- Complete the application form with black ink legibly and fully
- If you cannot visit, speak with the incumbent?
- Do you need this job, do you need this interview?
- Are your ready to answer questions (*on work, skills, audits, etc.*)?
- Are you physically prepared *(dress, bearing, speech, etc.)?*
- Do you look right *(dress, confidence, disposition, language)*?
- Are you mentally ready (*calm, confident and attentive*)?

• Do you have the appropriate documents?

Relax and do your best.

Further reading

1. Sudlow M, Toghill P. **How to be interviewed.** British Medical *Journal* 1996; 313: 2.

2. Burnet S. **How to perform well at your interview.** *BMJ* 2002; 324: S69

3. Spillane M. **Branding Yourself:** *how to look, sound and behave your way to success*. Pan Macmillan: London 2000.

7. Survive and thrive

To ensure your survival in the NHS, you must perform the duties of medical practitioner to the best of your ability.

7.1 Duties of a registered doctor

The duty of a registered doctor to a patient has been summarised by the GMC in *Good Medical Practice:*

Duties of a doctor registered with the GMC
- make the care of your patient your first concern;
- treat every patient politely and considerately;
- respect patients' dignity and privacy;
- listen to patients and respect their views;
- give patients information in a way they can understand;
- respect the rights of patients to be fully involved in decisions about their care;
- keep your professional knowledge and skills up to date;
- recognise the limits of your professional competence;
- be honest and trustworthy;
- respect and protect confidential information;
- make sure that your personal beliefs do not prejudice patient care;
- act quickly to protect patients from risk if you have good reason to believe that you or a colleague may not be fit to practise;
- avoid abusing your position as a doctor; and
- work with colleagues in the ways that best serve patients' interests.

7.2 Competition for SHO jobs

Competition for SHO jobs is very intense in some specialties- medicine and surgery in particular. This is expected. It has been mandatory for every medical graduate in the UK to work in surgery and medicine as an intern before full registration with the GMC. Most newly registered doctors seek

SHO jobs in medicine or surgery. Soon the PRHO will be able choose from a wider range of disciplines; something developing countries have offered their medical graduates for many decades!

7.3 Develop your CV
Getting your first job is one of many hurdles you must jump if you want to build a career in the medicine. To secure subsequent posts you need good references from your consultants. You must be short-listed for an interview before your consultant can praise you in a reference.

To be short-listed you must have sent a convincing CV to the recruiter. The ingredients of a persuasive CV take time and hard work to accumulate.

A winning CV grows with your career.
In addition to personal details and work history, a winning CV contains progressively sophisticated clinical audits, evidence of teaching skills, research studies, presentations and publications. Management and leadership skills and participation in clinical governance become progressively prominent with seniority.

The ingredients of a persuasive CV take time to master or acquire. Start now. Find a mentor to guide you. Join suitable organisations, learn to work with others, learn about clinical governance and risk management, do clinical audits and acquire essential non-clinical skills.

Take the membership or other appropriate exams as soon as you can so that you free to pay attention to non-clinical aspects of your career.

Fine-tune your English (spoken and written). If necessary take a course in medical writing.

The seedlings of future medical leaders and managers are planted quite early in one's medical career. Small successes in leadership may point to big future responsibilities. This is why small roles like organising duty rotas, co-ordinating juniors' teaching activities and the like are sought and rewarded in the assessment of a candidate's CV.

Work conscientiously, effectively and efficiently to achieve good clinical outcomes and to enhance your chances of getting a good reference.

You should be able to motivate yourself, show initiative, but ask for guidance and support in activities you are not familiar with (you are a trainee).

Learn (even if it means going on a course) how to relate to patients, clinical colleagues and other hospital staff.

Attitude to work, time, and initiative are important. The GMC asks the following questions about a doctor's attitudes to work:

Attitudes
Reliability and probity
Is this doctor dependable? Does he/she display honesty and integrity? Does he/she always act in the best interests of patients?

Initiative
Does this doctor show an appropriate degree of initiative?

Timekeeping
Is this doctor punctual and reliable? Does he/she contact the unit to warn of a problem?

7.4 Mind your business
As an intern you knew what was expected of you. Somebody had a duty to point you in the right direction. From SHO onwards you will have no minders. Of course if your work is unsatisfactory, if you neglect your duties, somebody will call you to task; may even discipline you.

Administration
Is this doctor efficient in the management of his/her own time and professional activities? Can he/she be relied upon to deal with the tasks required?

7.4.1 Claiming your privileges

If you are overworked and do not discuss it with your employer, if you do not claim legitimate travel expenses, if you do not use your study leave to attend courses, nobody will do it for you.

If you neglect your interest, it is nobody's business to remind you. It is not your consultant's, your clinical tutor's, the postgraduate dean's or any other official's job to be your minder. They will advise you if you ask them, but they are not your minders.

7.4.2 Asking for help

There are people willing and happy to help you, if you ask them. If you do not, they will leave you alone. If you ask your consultants sooner rather than later you will find somebody to review your CV or coach you for an interview.

If you do not ask for help you will not receive it. So *learn to ask for help* clearly and politely, saying *"please"* and *"thank you"* at the right time and in the right circumstances.

7.4.3 Seek advice sooner rather than later

If you do not seek your consultant's advice he/she is unlikely to force it on you. You should clarify in your mind, the issues you need advice on. Better still, you should consider available options and seek help in choosing the better or best of them.

If you have no information about a subject, search the internet, ask your hospital librarian for help. Librarians are trained to refine questions and make searches.

It is your duty, your responsibility, to look out for yourself, to seek guidance as necessary, to mind your own business.

7.4.4 "How do they manage it?"

Doing an excellent clinical job is important, but not enough if you want to attain the goals that brought you to Britain and PLAB.
Sanjit, a young man I know, recently received a professional shock. He is a very hard working senior house officer. He attends clinics, does ward rounds, clerks patients, writes good clinical letters, collects pathology samples- does all that is expected of a good SHO.

*He recently noticed consultants congratulating fellow SHOs on passing
membership exams and some on being appointed to SpR posts.*

"How did they manage it?" he asked himself.
*   He consulted* BMJ Careers *and* www.bmj.com, *found adverts for
registrar jobs and sent off for details.*

*The application forms were difficult to complete. He did not have the
information many sections required. His CV had not grown beyond the
PRHO experience*

*Sanjit sought advice from his consultant. After reading his CV, she gently
pointed out that she found no mention of clinical audits, advanced life
support skills, courses attended, presentations, research and publication,
nor of membership of a medical royal college.*
*   "Unless you acquired some of those attributes", she told him, "you are
unlikely to be short-listed for SHO jobs in future, let alone SpR posts."*

*How did Sanjit get into such a pickle? He did not set aside time for clinical
audits, case presentations, attending course, let alone doing research. He
does not take study leave no sit membership exams. He just works, eats,
sleeps and watches TV in between.*

You could face similar difficulties if, in addition to excellent clinical
performance, you do not also attend to non-clinical aspects of you career.

7.5 Find a mentor

A mentor is "a trusted teacher or adviser, an experienced or senior
colleague that helps and advises a junior". Your mentor should be a wise
senior doctor, who understands how the British health care system works
and is happy and willing to advice you about it.

A mentor acts as a sounding board for ideas, help you solve problems, acts
as a referee, empathises with you, acts as a coach, mirrors your ideas and
can be confided in. Not every consultant or GP principal can fill all of these
roles!
The consultant who offered you the clinical attachment will most likely

write a reference for your first job. He may continue as your mentor for a while. Later you may have to ask other senior doctors you admire or who have been recommended, to mentor you.

During your medical career you will change mentors as your mentoring needs change. Choose wisely. The mentor should be knowledgeable, approachable and happy to talk to you informally. He/ she should be somebody you can ring and talk to.
A mentor should help you to:
• Establish yourself quickly in the new work and social environment
• Understand the organisation and culture of British medicine
• Develop values and an ethical perspective on British healthcare
• Understand appropriate behaviour in different situations
• Overcome obstacles and setbacks and learn from them
• Acquire an open, flexible attitude to learning
• Enjoy the challenges of working in a new culture.

Read *"Mentoring- supporting doctors at work and play"*, an article published recently in the *BMJ* by Dr C Gringer (*BMJ* 2002; 324: s203).

7.6 Professional organisations
Of necessity doctors must join certain professional organisation either by law or by choice. *Registration with the General Medical Council is a legal requirement for medical practice.* Joining the BMA is voluntary.

Medical defence organisations
The NHS indemnifies its clinicians for legal problems arising from NHS work. The indemnity does not cover medical practice outside the NHS (private practice and Good Samaritan medical acts).

It is therefore advisable for doctors to maintain membership of a medical defence organisation.

Medical Defence Union (MDU): **www.the-mdu.com**
Medical Protection Society (MPS): **www.mps.org.uk**

In *Good Medical practice,* the GMC advises doctors to make sure that they have adequate insurance and professional advice:

Indemnity insurance
33. In your own interests, and those of your patients, you must obtain adequate insurance or professional indemnity cover for any part of your practice not covered by an employer's indemnity scheme.

NHS indemnity may not cover you for:
• claims from Non-NHS work (voluntary work, private practice, Good Samaritan acts)

• preparing statements for coroners and giving evidence at inquests

• GMC complaints procedures when legal advice may be essential

• NHS disciplinary procedures and suspensions.

The MDU will advice its members on medico-legal problems. This is important if the doctor disagrees with the employer on a course of action in a medico-legal complaint.

British Medical Association (BMA)
The BMA represents its members in industrial (work related) disputes. It collectively negotiates employment terms (salary, holidays, etc) for its membership with the Department of Health. Terms agreed between the BMA and the employer apply to non-members too.

In the past many doctors joined the BMA to get the BMJ. The journal is now accessible free on the internet. Will BMA membership decline?

7.7 Working with colleagues
Health care is delivered by groups of professionals. Interpersonal relationships strongly influence the outcome of your career. It colours the reference your consultant writes about you.
Good Medical Practice says the following about clinical teams:

Clinical teams include colleagues in other health professions...To be effective, medical and clinical teams must be well led and managed.

They must:
- have a positive attitude to patients and listen to their wishes and needs;
- make themselves aware of what patients think about the quality of their service; and
- have a clear understanding of their professional values, standards and purpose.

Team members must be willing to learn; committed to providing good-quality service and effective clinical practice; and open and honest about professional performance, both together and separately. ....

An effective team will show:
- purpose and values- for example, evidence of well-defined values, standards, functions and responsibilities, and strategic direction;

- performance- for example, evidence of leadership, competent management, good systems, good performance records and effective internal performance monitoring and feedback;

- consistency- for example, evidence of thoroughness and a systematic approach to providing patient care;

- effectiveness and efficiency- for example, evidence that they are assessing the care they provide, and of its clinical results;

- a chain of responsibility- for example, evidence that responsibilities are well defined and understood; accountability

- openness- for example, willingness to let others see in, and evidence of

  performance presented in ways that people outside the team can understand; and

- overall acceptability......... .inspire the trust and confidence of patients, employers, and professional colleagues.

7.7.1 Courtesy and politeness

You should be courteous and polite in your dealings with other people in the trust. Each person has a role, a job to do, be it grand or modest.

7.7.2 Professional relationships

The GMC has the following questions about professional relationships:

Professional relationships

Professional relationships with patients

Does this doctor establish and maintain the trust of patients? Does he/she listen to and respect their views, and their right to be involved in decisions about their care? Does he/she respect confidentiality and the privacy and dignity of patients? Is he/she accessible? Does he/she respond honestly and constructively to complaints or if things go wrong?

Working with other doctors

Is this doctor accessible? Does he/she work constructively as part of the clinical team? Does he/she respect the skills and contributions of others?

Working with other health care professionals

Is this doctor accessible? Does he/she respect the skills and contributions of other health care workers? Does he/she delegate, consult and refer appropriately?

7.7.3 Saying 'Please' and 'thank you'

Some cultures show their politeness and appreciation for services rendered without constantly saying *'please, thank you'*. From the tone of voice and disposition one is able to judge whether the speaker is polite or rude. The British prefer you to say *"please"* and *"thank you."*

In Britain one must say "please" *with every request and* "thank you" *on receipt of a service, big or small. It took me years to appreciate the importance of the simple word-"* please*". 'Would you please hand me the syringe" or some other item. It was difficult to say* 'Thank you' *for minor and expected services. But that is the British way of life. So I have learnt to say* "please" *and* "thank you." *Now I say* "thank you very much" *when handed a paper clip!*

7.7.4 Call her/him by name

People, even small children, prefer to be called by their names. They dislike *"You, hey you, nurse, you there,* etc." If you do not know a somebody's name, get her attention by politely saying: *"Would you please excuse me madam, miss...."* Introduce yourself and then state the help you need from her. Ask them for their name(s). Use the name to thank her/him for helping you. *"Thank you Miss Jones... Mrs Kaur... Mr Smith."*

Take every opportunity to learn your colleague's names. If you have forgotten ask again and use it to thank them for telling you.

7.7.5 Teams and teamwork

Prospective employers want to know if you relate well with professional colleagues. They want to know if you will fit into their organisations.

In hospitals, *colleague* means everybody you work with regularly (doctors, nurses, managers, etc.). There is no place for abrupt or rude behaviour in dealing with other professionals or support staff.

Learn to work harmoniously with all these *'colleagues'*. Observe native doctors and judge the level of contribution expected.

The GMC asks the following questions about a doctor's interpersonal skills:

Communication skills
Does this doctor give the patient the information he/she asks for or needs about her/his condition, its treatment and prognosis, in a way the patient can understand? Does he/she communicate adequately with colleagues and other health care professionals?

Generally British junior doctors speak forcefully and directly to their seniors and engage in disputation more strongly than junior doctors in India, for example. Do not imitate bad habits, though. Speak if you have something to say or in response to a question.

Much is talked and written about teams and teamwork in the NHS. However when something goes wrong there is a frantic search for an individual to blame. So contribute your (individual) best to teams.

7.7.6 Observe and learn from the natives
I have named some of the things you should, in your professional work, observe and study. You will receive no lectures on any of them. *Observe how native doctors relate to each other, other staff and to patients.'* Learn and emulate good practice. This does not mean abandoning your culture but accepting that *When in Rome you behave like the Romans.* When you return home, you will resume your *'normal'* behaviour.

7.7.7 Helping colleagues
If you can afford it, and often you can, swap work with colleagues who have urgent need to change work commitments. However do not become a soft touch. Note who owes favours and claim them back.

Relating to individuals and teams means:
• Saying *'please'* and *'thank you'* more often than ever before
• Being *obviously* courteous and polite more than before
• Sorting out work related problems with colleagues and helping
• Contributing to clinical and social activities
• *Observing and learning from the natives.*

7.8 Nurturing a career
A number of clinical and non-clinical activities (management skills, training, attending courses, research and audits, case presentations, publications, computer literacy, etc.) are vital for career development. You should start early and acquire these skills. They are essential to a winning CV and answering questions at interviews.

7.8.1 Courses attended
Two weeks in every 6 months should be spent on study leave- attending a course, preparing for membership exams, learning new skills or other activity relevant to your career. Your employer is expected to meet the costs.

In this section I include important courses I have attended recently. I list courses on the basis of clinical relevance or contribution to personal development:

Annual Meeting of the British Association for Community Child Health, University of Leicester, September 2002.

7.8.2 Clinical audit

Why do you need audits or research studies? I have explained before that your CV should grow with the passage of time. Clinical audit is one of the signs of growth. It is not too difficult to identify an important clinical or service issue to audit. The audit should be thorough and the report written well. An audit every six months is not too taxing.

Find the time and opportunity to do your audit. If your job lasts 6 months, ensure that your audit is completed before you leave the post, unless a reliable collaborator will complete it after you have left.

Most hospital doctors do not expect and should not be asked to do elaborate medical research. However they can join collaborative clinical studies.

This should not stop you from considering research on the interface between clinical medicine, sociology and psychology- *attitudes, belief, and behaviour* in personal health. Example:

Why won't a hypertensive, diabetic and obese man exercise more and eat less when he knows that exercise and weight loss would make the control of his hypertension and diabetes much easier?

Tough question! It does require expertise and tenure not available to an SHO or registrar. But who said you would remain an SHO or registrar? You can think of simpler socio-medical and psychological problems to investigate.

7.8.3 List audits and research in your CV

In a short CV, research and audit are described under *"research and audit"*. As your career grows and you accumulate audits and research studies, you need separate subheadings.

Prepare a brief summary of the audit, along the lines of the 'Abstract' of published papers, but shorter. Add the summary to the *'Audit'* section of your CV.

RSV infection in babies admitted for paediatric intensive care with bronchiolitis, Royal Catsford Infirmary (Dec. 2000 to Feb. 2001).

Case notes of 57 babies discharged from the paediatric intensive care unit with a diagnosis of bronchiolitis over three winter months were analysed.

Collection of naso-paharyngeal aspirates for RSV was recorded in 47 (82%). A result of RSV test was found in 43/57 (75%). A positive result was returned in 39 (83 %) of those tested.

RSV testing and lab report should be recorded in case notes. The audit should be repeated after the next bronchiolitis epidemic.

Please note the amount of detail given in the summary. It volunteers answers to *"what, where, when* and *how"* of clinical audit: *what* was done, *where* it was done, *when* it was done, *how* it was done, *what* was found and *what* should follow the audit.

7.8.4 Presentations
Present your audit and research studies at local hospital, regional or occasionally national meetings. Good audit studies are publishable (in journals).

In this section one would list audits and research presented at professional meetings. Examples:

> **The clinical course of Kawasaki's syndrome.** *Weekly Medical Grand Round, Catsford General Hospital, October 2002.*

7.8.5 Publications
If two doctors of otherwise equal abilities and experience apply for a job, the doctor with publications to his name will often be preferred. I know this may be unfair. The doctor with no publications may be a better clinician.

However there is no way of telling. There is bias in favour of the published doctor. So start early and get published.

Getting published takes time (developing ideas, doing the audit or research, analysing the data, writing the paper and finding a journal that will publish it). It is not something you can do the weekend before sending off your CV in response to an advert in *BMJ Careers*.

7.8.6 Management/leadership skills
In this category you would include your role in organising, persuading or leading others in some activity.

Running meetings (scheduling, writing the agenda, chairing, writing minutes) becomes important with seniority. Many multidisciplinary meetings are often badly run because of lack of training and experience.

The following are some of the entries one is glad to see under *Management/ leadership* in CVs. Did you do (have you done) any of these things? Are you learning or doing something similar?
- served as captain of the hospital rugby football team
- organised teaching programme for fellow senior house officers
- serve as regional secretary to BMA junior doctors' committee
- serving president of the hospital doctors mess
- secretary of Catsford Writers' Society,…etc.

7.8.7 Teaching/training
The GMC asks the following questions about involvement in teaching:

Teaching and training (if applicable)
Not all trainees will be involved in teaching or training others. If so:
Does this doctor accept responsibility for teaching junior colleagues?
Does he/she ensure that juniors are properly supervised? Is he/she honest and objective in assessing the performance of others?

Under this heading you would list those activities in which you teach or supervise somebody in basic knowledge or practical skills:
- taught clinical medicine to medical students and house officers

- supervise new senior house officers in resuscitation of the newborn
- tutor in emergency orthopaedics and trauma for doctors new to A & E.

7.8.8 Other Skills

There are many non-clinical skills that enhance a doctor's employability and utility to his clinical team. These include:

- *Computing and information technology* (typing, graphics, website design, desktop publishing). Clinical units would welcome help in designing and producing patient education materials.

- *Foreign language(s)* are useful in multiethnic, multilingual Britain. Sometimes patients do not receive services they should until an interpreter has been found.

  List the languages you speak, for which you could translate for a patient.

- *Writing skills* are useful in developing, editing and producing patient education/information booklets and leaflets. Some clinical teams have published books for sale.

7.9 When is full registration?

You know that your student Visa will expire. Are you ready for that? When will you be eligible for full registration?

In October 2002, the GMC issued new guidance on moving from limited to full registration. The following has been culled from the GMC website **www.gmc-uk.org.uk**). Please visit the site for full details.

7.9.1 Legibility for full registration.

¥ satisfactorily completion of 12 month's UK experience as an SHO or SpR in the previous two years in substantive or locum posts of at least three month's duration.

¥ appointment to a Type 1 Specialist Registrar post after satisfactorily completion of 12 month's UK experience as an SHO grade in the last two years.

¥ eligibility for inclusion in the Specialist Register (as confirmed by notification of eligibility from the Specialist Training Authority (STA), of the Royal Colleges or its successor.

To move from limited to full registration, a doctor must demonstrate knowledge, skills and attitudes equal to those of a competent Senior House Officer (SHO) in relation to standards of competence, care and conduct described in *Good Medical Practice*. The GMC sends this booklet to all registered doctors. Read it in print or online at ***www.gmc-uk.org.uk.***

7.9.2 Standards of competence
Every consultant you have worked with in the UK will be asked to complete a report on your performance according to the following:
• Good medical practice
• Treatment in emergencies
• Maintaining good medical practice
• Professional relationships
• Communication skills
• Teaching and training (if applicable)
• Attitudes
• Administration
• Occupational health.

The consultant is asked to indicate on a standard form: ***Standard Achieved, Standard Not Achieved*** or ***Not Assessed***, as appropriate.

7.10 When to seek registrar posts
In the past SHOs sought registrar posts when they felt competent enough to perform the duties of a registrar. This was usually after two years working as an SHO. It was not necessary to have gained the membership.

7.10.1 The new paradigm
Most medical specialties only give SpR posts to doctors with the full membership. A few will appoint a doctor to an SpR post after 2 years as an SHO and part 1 of the membership. So the sooner you pass your the membership, the earlier you can apply for registrar posts.

There is little to be gained from continuing as an SHO after your membership, unless you have just started a competitive (desirable) subspecialty job (like cardiology, neurology, gastroenterology or respiratory medicine). Then continue with the posting and apply for SpR jobs towards the end of the appointment.

7.10.2 Foreigners linger in SHO posts
SHOs who graduated abroad linger in SHO jobs while local graduates quickly move to general practice, registrar jobs or non-medical careers. Perhaps the foreign graduates think that a doctor has to be very skilled before he can work as a registrar

The local graduate appreciates that provided he/she knows can manage common emergencies, advice on difficult cases can always be sought from the consultant. So he /she seeks and gets an SpR post.

There is little to be gained (*in advancing your career*) from working as an SHO long after your membership.

7.10.3 Foreign doctors fill non-training posts
There are several reasons why foreign doctors form the majority of non-training non-career grades (clinical fellow, trust doctor, staff grade and the like). It could be that the doctor:
• has not passed the membership exams
• has passed the membership exams but has not secured an SpR post
• has the membership, but wants more experience before seeking an SpR post.

7.11 Stop! It's non-training
The Department of Health (DoH) and the royal medical colleges have not allowed the creations of adequate SHO and registrar posts for the amount work that needs to be done. The DoH has also agreed that junior doctors should work a certain number of hours per week and should have set times to rest during working hours. This has left hospitals with a shortage of junior doctors.

Hospitals are creating alternate job titles to avoid DoH and college restrictions on numbers of junior doctors in training posts. Clinical fellow

(*SHO work*) and senior clinical fellow, trust doctor, staff grade (*registrar work*) posts have mushroomed.

However these have major limitations on the individual doctors filling them. *BMJ Careers* warns about the dangers of taking such jobs. What are the limitations of non-training posts? Are they important?

- The posts are not recognised for professional training. Time spent in them does not count toward recognition by the GMC as a specialist.

- Non-training junior doctors are not party agreements negotiated between the BMA Junior Doctors' Committee and the DoH. They do not have the same privileges as traditional training grades although the two cadres may be working side by side.

- Clinical fellow posts (junior and senior) are short term, like long locums and contribute little to future professional careers. There is no job security. Appointments are for a year or two at time.

- The medical royal colleges and postgraduate deans do not recognise the existence of non-training junior doctors. Would you volunteer to join such a cadre?

- Trust and staff grade posts have tenure, but their experience does not count towards the requirements for recognition as a specialist. Trust and staff grade doctors are neither *junior doctors* nor *consultants* and do not enjoy the privileges of either group.

- Trust and staff grade doctors may be asked to perform consultant duties without equivalent support, recognition or remuneration. Late in 2002, the BMA has established *"Staff and Associate Specialists Committee"* to voice the interests of non consultant career grades.

- After a period in clinical fellowship, trust or staff grade posts the doctor may find it difficult to return to regular training posts.

I would not take up such posts unless it is unavoidable: *"take the job or become unemployed"*. I would then strive to get out as soon as possible.

7.12 Abandon specialty

It is very hard to give up something you have for a long time, planned, dreamed about, wanted and hoped to achieve. It is painful and many people keep postponing the decision till it is too late to change. Many doctors linger in specialties repeating SHO jobs, doing locums, and taking up non-training junior grades in the hope that one day they will land the coveted SpR job. The longer you stay in junior grades the less likely you are to progress.

7.12.1 Blinded by love

I have heard of a doctor who repeated the full internship in the UK followed by 6 months' work as SHO in specialty X. Then he hit roadblocks; he could not find SHO jobs in the specialty.

In his unusual wisdom or following advice, he has completed 12 months clinical attachment in the same discipline. He must be in love with X. After the 6 months as SHO in a specialty, how does an extra attachment improve his CV? What will he *observe* that will be interesting at job interviews? How would he answer the question: *After 6 months as SHO in X, why did you return to clinical attachments?* The question will not be asked. He is unlikely to be short-listed for interview.

Does he believe that the clinical attachment will help him get SHO jobs in his beloved X? Sorry, it will not. It only confirms his failure to progress in the discipline. When will he notice/ appreciate *that he is wasting time (and money)?* What should he do?

7.12.2 When to abandon old loves

He should abandon the specialty, change to another discipline right away. He has ruined his CV by repeating a clinical attachment after 18 months of medical practice in the UK. His action is, without clinical evidence of a nervous or psychological deficit, like an adult giving up walking in favour of crawling.

7.12.3 Find a new suitor

If surgery, obstetrics and gynaecology, paediatrics, medicine and their subspecialties jilt you, try your charm in general practice, psychiatry, pathology, geriatrics (care of the elderly) the pharmaceutical industry or some other less crowded discipline. It is better to be comforted by a second love than to die of a broken heart. Many doctors have found comfort and prosperity in their second choice of specialty.

Please do not abandon one competitive specialty for another where jilting suitors is equally routine practice. Find a specialty that has recently fallen out of favour or has never been fashionable. Consult your mentors and true friends. Your second choice should have opportunities for career progress. Fashion in medical specialties changes rapidly (few years). Specialties that were unfashionable get crowded when rumours that *"the future is brighter in Y"* circulate in doctors' common rooms or on the internet. Track down the new fashions- *the news*. Do not base your decisions to change specialty on old stories or rumours.

7.13 What is clinical governance
The NHS executive (governing body) defines clinical governance as:

"A framework through which NHS organisations are accountable for continuously improving the quality of their services and safeguarding high standards of care by creating an environment in which excellence in clinical care will flourish." www.chi.nhs.uk/

7.13.1 What does this mean?
Continuously improving = training, audit, professional development.
Safeguarding standards = clinical guidelines, audit, CHI inspections.

To me, a simple clinician, clinical governance means:
• insuring that the patient gets effective clinical care,
• is not hurt by the clinical care or the environment, and
• the clinician (me) and my health care trust don't get sued.

7.13.2 The Commission for Health Improvement (CHI)
CHI is the agency charged with advancing and ensuring effective clinical governance in the NHS. At the heart of CHI's work is the patient's experience of the NHS. It aims to improve the quality of patient care and raise standards by:

• assessing every NHS organisation and making its findings public
• investigating when there is serious failure

- checking that the NHS is following national guidelines
- advising the NHS on best practice.

The clinician is encouraged to follow established clinical guidelines, to check his/her practice (audit) and to ensure his/her clinical knowledge and skills are sound (training and continuous personal development).

7.13.3 Organisations driving clinical governance

The following are the major organisations driving clinical governance:

Academy of Medical Royal Colleges	www.aomrc.org.uk/
British Association of Medical Managers	www.bamm.co.uk/
Clinical Governance Support team	www.cgsupport.org.uk/
Commission for Health Improvement's	www.chi.nhs.uk/
The Department of Health	www.doh.gov.uk/
Health Professions Council	www.hpcuk.org/
Institute of Healthcare Improvement	www.ihi.org/
Institute of Healthcare Management	www.ihm.org.uk/
Modernisation Agency	www.modernnhs.uk/
National Audit Office	www.nao.gov.uk
National Clinical Assessment Authority	www.ncaa.nhs.uk/
National Institute for Clinical Excellence	www.nice.org.uk/
National Patient Safety Agency	www.npsa.org.uk/
NHS Information Authority	www.nhsia.nhs.uk/
Parliamentary and Health Service Ombudsman	
	www.ombudddssman.org.uk
Patients' Association	www.patientsassociation.com/main/htm

Many other organisations have significant interest and influence in clinical outcomes and clinical governance. The CHI website, *www.chi.nhs.uk*, will lead you to their internet addresses.

7.13.4 What is clinical risk?

Clinical risk is the likelihood that a patient will suffer harm as a result of a clinical intervention or lack of it.

Hospital risks may be clinical (wrong diagnosis, wrong treatment, inaction, faulty equipment, etc.) or environmental (wet floors, falling ceilings, etc.). The GMC has the following question about risk management:

> **Occupational health**
> Does this doctor follow safe practices relating to chemical, physical and psychological hazards in the workplace?

Therefore risk management includes managing, controlling or preventing clinical and non-clinical causes of harm in a clinical setting.

You should appreciate how clinical governance and risk management work. Learn when and how to use clinical guidelines.

7.14 Fine-tune your English

Even though you did pass the language test before the medical PLAB, your spoken and written English can still benefit from fine-tuning. Becoming fluent in English as it is spoken in Britain is not easy. The habits acquired abroad are difficult to change.

The way you write and speak English will continue to impact on the impression you create at work and in job searches. It is worth your effort to fine-tune your English.

Listen to the radio (BBC World Service, BBC Radio 4, Voice of America) when you have the time. It will help you master the English idiom. CNN, ITV News, BBC24, Sky News and EuroNews use excellent English in their news broadcasts. Learn to write and speak English like the British (or the Americans).

7.15 Dress sense

What we wear has an impact on how other people see us. Smartly dressed individual are generally assumed to be smart, more intelligent than their shabbier colleagues (unless they are professors!).

Cultivate a sense of what clothes are suitable in medical environments. It is better to be conservative than to be fashionable and risk offending clients and superior. The comments made about dressing for interview apply to dressing for regular work.

Smart dressing does not mean expensive clothes. One can dress smartly but relatively cheaply by careful selection of material that washes well and keeps shape after ironing. Ties are essential for male doctors. Females should shun tops that expose part of the trunk (belly button and waist) and excess cleavage.

7.16 Abandon medicine?

To some people it is a blasphemy to suggest that a doctor should abandon medicine and seek a livelihood in some other activity. A number of medical graduates have built successful careers outside medicine. Some graduate MB ChB but do not bother with internship and registration as medical practitioners. Many go into banking and business consulting.

Other graduates do internship, embark on a medical career, but change their minds at SHO or registrar level. In American young doctors are taking master of business administration (MBA) degrees and going into health care management.

More commonly in Britain doctors join the pharmaceutical (drug) industry as medical advisors after a time as registrar in hospital medicine or as young GP principals.

Forgive me for suggesting you abandon medicine. The thought has crossed my mind too a few times. I have not acted on it because:
• my dependants need a regular source of income (my salary)
• the financial consequences (salary cut) would be punishing
• I am now too old to be recruited by reputable organisations.

Old doctors are unlikely to change specialties or abandon medicine.

7.17 Is everything OK?

Try to gauge how well you relate to people you work with.
• How to you get on with consultants, nurses and others professionals?
• Have you felt that things are not as good as they should be?
Sometimes, things may be going badly but nobody is brave enough to tell you. It is, unfortunately, a common problem in the UK. Sometimes you are the last to hear about your problems.

If uneasiness develops between you and people you previously related to easily, ask a trusted colleague if he/she is aware of some problems relating to you- work performance, personal issues, offence committed or whatever. Ask your consultant directly if all is well with your clinical performance and interpersonal relationships. But tread carefully.

Are you achieving your goals?
- How many audits, presentations and publications have you done?
- How are you getting on with the membership- passed it yet?

Summary
- Join a medical protection organisation (the MDU, MPS or other).

- Develop your curriculum vitae as you progress in the NHS. There is no time to waste. Your CV needs them to grow as time passes.

- Learn to speak English like the British. Say *'please'* and *'thank you'* to lubricate social and professional interactions.

- Play on clinical teams effectively. Appreciate other health professionals.

- Participate in clinical governance, risk management and clinical audit. Acquire management and leadership skills (in small doses!).

- Mind your business. Keep an open ear and a sharp eye. Is your career thriving?

Further reading

1. Handy CB. **Understanding Organisations**. Penguin Books 1997

2. Scoote M, Thaventhiran J, Elkington A. **Progress towards higher specialist training.** *BMJ* 2002; 325: s49

3. Gringer C. **Mentoring- supporting doctors at work and play.** *BMJ* 2002; 324: s203

4. GMC. **Good medical practice.** 3rd edition 2001

5. Dosani S, Adsett J. **The staff grade dilemma.** *BMJ* 2002; 325: s170

6. MacDonald R. **Top tips for getting through the system and having a successful career in the UK.** *BMJ* 2002; 325: s172-s173

8. Postgraduate education

8.1 Origin of royal colleges

The royal medical colleges evolved from associations of doctors with special interest in an aspect of medicine working to advance their specialism. Tradition dictated that these associations seek *'protection'* from the monarch (king or queen). This was *granted* as a *royal charter* (permit) for the associations to peruse its specialism under royal protection.

First there were royal college of physicians in London, Edinburgh and Glasgow (physicians practise physic- *the art or practice of healing*), then royal colleges of surgeons (branch of barbers- who cut hair and lanced boils). More colleges (for obstetricians, pathologists, ophthalmologists, radiologists and paediatricians) have been formed as offshoots of the Royal College of Physicians of London. The college of anaesthetists has just broken loose from the surgeons' grip.

The Academy of Royal Medical Colleges has been formed to bring the royal medical colleges together (to co-ordinate their activities) in medicine, patient care and socio-medical advocacy.

8.2 Training for general practice

After PRHO jobs the doctor serves in at least four- 6 months hospital posts followed by a year as a registrar in general practice. On completing the rotations, the doctor is enrolled on the list of trained GPs- who may become GP principals. Only fully trained doctors are allowed to become principal GPs. Most doctors who want to become GPs succeed.

The GP trainee may, if he so wishes, take exams for the membership of the Royal College of General Practitioners (MRCGP). Unlike other medical specialties, it is not mandatory to have the MRCGP before he/she can become a registrar in general practice.

PLAB graduates and general practice training

If you had to do PLAB, there are hurdles to jump before you can dream of training in general practice:

- You must be fully registered before your can apply
- You require permits that are rather difficult to obtain.

If you are interested in general practice you should make appropriate enquiries very early. Unfortunately as a PLAB graduate you are not allowed to transfer from hospital jobs into general practice like UK and other European graduates can do. Consult the GP Tutor at your postgraduate medical centre about the authorities to approach.

8.3 Hospital careers

The PRHO year is followed by about 3 years as SHO in a hospital specialty. The membership is usually obtained in this period. Some SHOs then join the specialist registrar (SpR) training cadre where they serve for about 4-5 years before getting a Certificate of Completed Specialist Training (CCST). With the CCST the doctor is ready to become a consultant (in his speciality).

Some doctors elect to become GPs and join GP training others fail to secure SpR posts and either seek work among non-training hospital grades (short term, or tenured), gain tenure in non-consultant career grades or leave medical practice for the pharmatheutical industry or other careers. Most non-consultant career grade doctors are foreign graduates.

8.4 Future of the SHO grade

There are problems in the numbers and opportunities for professional training beyond SHO. *"Unfinished Business: Proposals for Reform of the Senior House Officer Grade"*, a consultation document on the future of the SHO cadre was published in August 2002. It proposes integrating the PRHO, SHO and registrar grades.

The problem is not the grading, but insufficiency of posts at SHO and registrar levels and lack of career opening for SHOs. Will integration without change in the number of doctors, workloads or career openings for the SHO, solve the problem?

8.5 Membership exams

Each college sets examinations for doctors who want to join its membership. Senior members are promoted to fellows.

Membership exams are usually split into 2 parts, rarely 3. You must pass the earlier part before moving to the next. Royal colleges publish their regulations in booklets and on the internet.

After passing the final part of the membership exam, the doctor is admitted to the college as a member and granted a diploma of membership. It is not a university degree, but a certificate to show that the doctor is a member of the royal college and is entitled to its privileges and responsibilities as set out in the college's royal charter.

8.5.1 Studying for the membership

Doctors study for membership exams when and where they can. There are no university courses for these exams. However, entrepreneurial individuals, hospital departments and business companies have set up fee-charging courses for these exams. The courses are advertised in *BMJ Careers* and on ***www.bmj.com.***

8.5.2 Preparing for membership exams

Without a career plan time will fly past you; by the time you wake up it will be later than you thought. Get the membership before you lose the enthusiasm for exams.

Courses, mock exams and advice on the web

MRCOG survival courses: www.mrcogcourses.co.uk
MRCPsych online study forum: www.superego-café.com
MRCP and MRCPCH courses, mock exams: www.123doc.com
MRCPath revision notes: www.ich.ucl.ac.uk/cmgs/cmgshelp.thm
Anaesthesia: www.FRCA.co.uk
Radiology teaching: www.radiology.co.uk
Surgery MCQs: www.surgeons.org.uk
Ophthalmology MCQs, slides, courses: www.MRCOPHTH.com

After S. Dosani, Hospital Doctor, www.hospital-doctor.net *10th Oct. 2002*

Websites appear and disappear. Talk to other doctors studying for the same exam; they may tell you of new websites.

Just as you did for PLAB, set yourself targets. Use every opportunity to study and prepare for your membership:

- *Read the most recent guidelines* from *'your'* royal college. Most colleges publish them on the internet.

- *Set a time table,* fix dates as appropriate. When will you sit part 1? When will you sit part 2, etc. Develop a study schedule (daily reading, attending seminars, course, etc.). What studying have you done today?

- *Carry a small book* to read in free moments- waiting for ward rounds, when patients misses clinic appointments, etc. An A4 size bag, with a fastener to stop your books (sandwich and can of cola) from flying out, is essential in paediatrics and psychiatry where the need/rationale for white coats does not exist.

- *Use your study leave to attend a membership course* to get the 'feel' of the exam and to appreciate that other doctors face similar difficulties.

- *Carry a book of exams questions* on you as the exam approaches (you do have at least three?) Practice/revise in 'free moments'.

- *Don't mark the answers.* However faint, marks ruin questions for the next round of self testing. You *want to know that you 'know'* the answer without *the smudge around* a, d, *or* e. Use loose pieces of paper (post-its, free at 'drug lunches', are excellent) to jot down your answers.

- *Discussion/revision groups* have been useful to some candidates.

- *Check exam guidelines regularly.* Visit the college website, see if rules have changed and you have not heard about it.

Sanjit got into a pickle because he worked, ate, slept and watched TV. He had no career focus. He was happy as long as he earned a living; time and fellow SHOs left him behind.

8.6.3 Membership before SHO job?

I have met a few doctors who got the membership before working as SHO in the UK. In the past there was no problem with that. However with local doctors progressing to registrar soon after gaining the membership, there is a risk that in future recruiters might be biased against applicants who lingered in SHO jobs after their memberships.

The impression that the candidate *stayed in SHO posts longer than usual after the membership* and therefore is *'not progressing'* could hurt her/his career! Not progressing = unlikely to make registrar. Is it unfair? Yes it is. But who is giving awards for fairness?

8.6.4 Take your membership while an SHO

So if you can, avoid getting the full membership exam till you are an SHO. It is better to take part 1 of the membership, work as an SHO, and then take the final exam. As soon as you gain the membership, apply for SpR posts.

8.7 Higher degrees

For over half a century, if not longer, it has been fashionable for registrars to acquire second degrees before applying for a consultant posts. This has been an MD, ChM or occasionally a PhD. In Britain the MD is usually taken from the university that awarded the first degree.

Recently the MSc in a variety of disciplines has gained popularity. It is shorter (one to two academic years) and can be done part-time.

The PhD, an internationally recognised research degree takes 3 to 4 years to complete. Unlike the part-time MD, the PhD requires full time study to meet research requirements.

Most junior doctors can't afford the expenses or the time for a PhD. Some native graduates may take the MD from their university, but most native and immigrant doctors are happy with an MSc or ChM.

The MSc is usually modular and includes data interpretation, assessment of published material, statistical methods and several modules from the discipline in which the degree is offered. Unlike the MD or PhD, the MSc contains a strong taught component.

The choice (from PhD, MD or MSc) depends on what you want the degree for. If you want a career in research and academic medicine, do the PhD. The MD may be considered inadequate for leadership of research teams.

Although a higher degree is not mandatory for consultant or GP principal posts, when the competition is tough your MSc/ ChM/ MD or PhD could come to your aid.

8.8 Maintaining good medical practice

In current jargon *'Maintaining good medical practice'* is called *Continuing Professional Development (CPD)*. The assumption is that the doctor will continuously study and train to maintain her/his knowledge and skills, to learn more, to improve.

The GMC poses the following questions in relation to CPD:

Maintaining good medical practice

Basic science
Does this doctor have adequate knowledge of the physical, behavioural, epidemiological and clinical sciences upon which medicine depends?

Clinical knowledge and skills
Does this doctor possess an appropriate level of understanding of acute illness and of disabling and chronic diseases within the specialty, and of relevant interventions in acute and chronic illness?

Does he/she keep knowledge and skills up to date? Does he/she participate regularly in educational activities?

Does he/she take part in regular and systematic medical and clinical audit? Does he/she respond constructively to assessments and appraisals of professional competence and performance?

Ethical and legal framework of practice
Does this doctor observe and keep up to date with the laws and statutory codes which affect his/her work?

Summary
• postgraduate medical education is governed by the royal medical colleges, the GMC and specialist training committees

- royal medical colleges developed from special interest groups that sought and were granted royal charters

- membership means a doctor has passed exams set by a royal college and been admitted to the membership of that college

- general practice trainees do 4 hospital jobs and a year as registrar in general practice. The MRCGP is not mandatory.

- set study goals and schedules for membership exams; take them at the earliest opportunity (before you lose the motivation)

- it could be risky to gain the membership before SHO jobs. You risk being labeled *'not progressing'* - not registrar material

- the MSc is now an acceptable alternative to the MD.

Further reading

1. Leung W-C. **Giving and seeking career guidance.** *BMJ* 2001; 322: s2-7302.

2. Bache J. **Choosing a career.** *BMJ* 1999; 7193 Volume 318 (8 May)

3. Scoote M, Thaventhiran J, Elkington A. **Progress towards higher specialist training.** *BMJ* 2002; 325: s49

4. Anderson M, Jankowski J. **Higher research degrees: making the right choice.** *BMJ* 2001; 322: s2-7277.

5. Benson J. **Postgraduate exams: the MRCP(UK).** *BMJ* 2002; 325: s164.

—

9. Clinical documents

9.1 Purpose of clinical documents
Clinical documents record or document clinical activity or event in notes, letters or reports so that they can be consulted later (notes, letters) or used to pass on information (letters and reports) to distant individuals.

Letters convey information from writer or seek information. Reports communicate the findings of some deliberate study to the body that commissioned them or the general public.

9.2 Legal status of clinical documents
Clinical notes, letters and reports become legal documents as soon as they are made. They belong to the Secretary of State for Health (government). Patients have a legal right to see their notes and to receive copies, including X-rays and scans. Authorisation from a representative of the Secretary of State enables them o read the notes and /or get copies.

9.3 Preparing the document
Clinical documents are normally typed (or word-processed) by medical secretaries. The secretary types the document from a tape recorded by the clinician, a hand written script or from dictation notes.

9.3.1 Organising the content
Think out what you want to include and exclude from the letter or report. Use subheadings to structure the material. These may be included in the dictation or script and the typed document. Even if you do not want subheadings in the finished document you should organise the content along the same framework (see examples later).

9.3.2 Using a tape recorder
It is your duty to speak clearly so that the secretary can make out your words. Indicate where new paragraphs and essential punctuation marks should be- particularly the brackets [{( )}], comma (,), dash (-), the full stop or period (.).

Spell out unusual words. Name individuals and organisations you want to receive copies of the document.

Indicate how you want your name to appear on the document, which degree(s) to quote and the attribution- (SHO, Registrar to Dr Dorset...

9.3.3 Writing the hand script
Write so that the secretary can make out the words. Organise the contents along subheading framework even if you do not write the heading down.

Write your name, degrees and attributions in the way you want them to appear on the typed document. List individuals and organisations you wish to receive copies of the document.

9.3.4 Signing the document
Signing documents means more than scribbling your name in the proper place. It is your duty, before you sign the document, to ensure that it says what you wanted to say, not less and not more. You are legally responsible for its content. It goes out under your name.

The GMC offers the following advice:

Writing reports, giving evidence and signing documents
51. You must be honest and trustworthy when writing reports, completing or signing forms, or providing evidence in litigation or other formal inquiries.

This means that you must take reasonable steps to verify any statement before you sign a document. You must not write or sign documents which are false or misleading because they omit relevant information. If you have agreed to prepare a report, complete or sign a document or provide evidence, you must do so without unreasonable delay.

---

* Read carefully, the typed documents and check for errors in content, spelling, grammar and meaning, drugs (names, doses, preparations, frequency, etc.).

* Is the message expressed the way you wanted to express it? This is

important in medico- legal issues. Lawyers love discovering hidden meaning in unguarded expressions.

- Make appropriate corrections and get the document retyped. Next time prepare the manuscript or dictation more carefully. If the mistakes were your doing then apologise to the secretary.

- Only sign documents whose content you are happy with.

- Only a copy of the signed document should be kept (in patient's notes or other appropriate place).

9.4 Essentials of note making
When you make entries into patient notes or write a clinical letter, take care. Please:
- think of what you are going to write and how you will phrase it
- write politely; there is no need to record your rudeness
- avoid ambiguity, your message should be clear
- use simple, short words; short sentences and short paragraphs
- avoid superfluous words and phrases.

Basic note making
- Ensure the patient's names and hospital number are on the page
- Start by writing down the date and time
- Write legible, concise, clear and precise notes
- No empty lines between notes- write on all lines
- Record current medications, dosage, delivery method, devices
- Record consent from, advice to, discussion with patients/parents
- Enter laboratory results into body of notes as soon as you get them
- Record clinical progress, procedures and treatments regularly (at least daily and whenever there is a change in condition or clinical action
- Record unusual incidents; discuss them with senior doctor/sister
- Record future plans: 'Follow up' [when, whom, where], 'No Follow up'
- Record the date and time of discharge
- Sign and print your name after every entry.

9.5 Clinical letters

The aim of a clinical letter is to convey information or seek advice (consultation) or practical assistance (referral).

The content of the letter varies depending on the condition, severity and course of the condition and the addressee. Details included depend on when in the course of the clinical contact, the letter is written. Initial letters tend to be longer than subsequent ones.

9.5.1 References

Clinical letters quote references to identify the patient (hospital number, letter writer and the secretary (their initials).

9.5.2 Date of writing
9.5.3 Addressee's name and address
9.5.4 Patient's name (date of birth) and address

9.5.5 Clinical problem or diagnosis

If the diagnosis is known you should state it here. If a diagnosis has not been made the clinical problem(s) should used.

A patient is seen in the clinic with chronic abdominal pain and bloody diarrhoea. The first clinic letter might say:
    Problem: *Abdominal pain and bloody diarrhoea.*

Following investigations a diagnosis of *'Ulcerative colitis'* was made. Thereafter clinical letters about the same subject would say:
    Diagnosis: *Ulcerative colitis.*

If complications and problems arose then the diagnosis would be accompanied by a list of problems; like:
- *toxic megacolon*
- *erythema nodosum*
- *arthritis and spondylitis, etc.*

9.5.6 Treatment/medication/therapy

All treatments (drugs: dosage, preparation, route/devices, frequency, duration, etc.) should be stated as they would appear on a prescription. This will enable any doctor (GP or in hospital) to review treatment with the patient, and if necessary recommend changes. It is impossible to recommend changes if you are not sure of the dosage or its frequency.

*"**Becotide 2 puffs b.d**" was recorded in the patient's notes and clinic letter. How much Becotide was in the puff: 50mcg, 100mcg, 200mcg or 400mcg?*

9.5.7 History
The essentials of the history (symptoms, duration, past investigations and their results, past treatments and their effects) and patient's concerns.

9.5.8 Examination
Both positive and significant negative (absent) signs should be included in this section. Their interpretation should be given.

9.5.9 Investigations
Known results and their interpretation should be communicated. Planned investigations should be stated.

9.5.10 Recommendations and advice
Recommendations and advice given to the patient should be described:
> *"Advised to eat less and exercise more"* (hypertensive, overweight)
> *"Continue trimethoprim till he is out of nappies"* (baby with VUR).

9.5.11 Follow-up
Arrangements for 'follow-up' (subsequent clinic visits) should also be reported.
> *Will be seen in Mr Shah's clinic in 4 weeks*
> *Review every 3 months- check weight, BP and HbA1c*
> *Continue using splint for 6 weeks*
> *Discharged.*

9.6 Examples of clinical letters
In Britain every patient is supposed to be registered with a general practitioner (GP). GPs are contracted to manage health problems in the community. They supervise continuing treatment and decide when to refer to specialist care. They need information about the services their patients' received or did not receive in hospitals and clinics.

The examples are discharge summary, outpatient clinic letter, primary care referrals, intra-hospital referral and a letter to a patient/parent.

9.6.1 Hospital discharge summary

Brambleton General Hospital
Brambleton M75 9FT

Our Ref: X4534652

29 June 2001

Dr J Williams
Moss Lane Surgery
Duke Way
Brambleton M76 3EF

Dear Dr Williams

Re: Donald McDonald (born 12. 04. 2001)
45 Nottingham Close, Brambleton M76 8QL.

Admitted: 21.06.2001. **Discharged**: 27.06.2001.
Consultant: Dr M Gregory

Diagnoses: Grade 4 Vesico-Ureteric Reflux on Left
        E.coli Urinary Tract Infection

Prophylaxis: Trimethoprim 2mg/kg at night (now 10 mg)

History: Donald was off feeds and feverish for 2 days. Trimethoprim had been stopped. His parents said he had been well and needed no antibiotics.

Examination: He was miserable, febrile 39°C, but no other signs of infection.

Investigations: A clean catch urine sample had few red blood cells an >100 white cells. The E.coli isolated on urine culture was sensitive to cephalexin, ampicillin and trimethoprim.

Treatment: Donald received intravenous cephalexin for 5 days.

Advice: Antibiotic prophylaxis against UTI was discussed with his parents. The dose of trimethoprim liquid should be adjusted monthly according to his weight: 2mg /kg (0.2 ml/kg). His parents were given a leaflet on UTI.

Follow-up: Donald will be seen in Dr Gregory's clinic in 8 weeks.

Yours sincerely

VSatish

Vinkram Satish MRCP
Registrar to Dr M Gregory.

Dr Satish's letter to Dr Williams, the patient's GP, clearly:

• identifies the patient by name, age and address

• states when the child was admitted and discharged

• names the child's consultant, to whom inquiries may be directed

• names the reason for hospitalisation (E.coli UTI in Grade 4 left VUR)

• highlights home management- drug, dose regimen and current dose

• briefly describes the history (off feeds, feverish), physical findings (fever), investigations (urinalysis, urine culture and sensitivity),

• states hospital management (IV cephalexin for 5 days)

• states advice given (UTI prophylaxis with trimethoprim discussed; monthly dose adjustment: (0.2ml/kg); parents given leaflet on UTI)

• states future plans (Follow-up in Dr Gregory's clinic in 4 weeks).

Brambleton General Hospital
Brambleton M75 9FT

Our Ref Z0486873

29 July 2002

Dr J Williams
Moss Surgery
Moss Lane
Brambleton M76 4ZP

Dear Dr Williams

Re: Jennifer Lightheart (born 12.04.1986)
23 Magellan Drive, Brambleton M76 8DL.

Problem: Convulsions while working on a computer

Investigations: EEG, CT head

I saw Jennifer with her mother in Dr Hertz's clinic. Jennifer felt fuzzy
while working on computer at school, Tuesday 11th July 2000. She woke to
find herself on the classroom floor. Her teacher said Jennifer fell off a chair,
had jerking arms and legs for about 10 minutes; slept for 20 minutes and
was drowsy for a while afterwards.

There was no history of fits or chronic headaches; school work is excellent.
A twin sister is treated for photosensitive epilepsy.

Her weight and height were on the 75th centile. Her skin was normal. Her BP
was 120/65 mmHg; cranial nerves, optic fundi and reflexes were normal

Dr Hertz saw Jennifer and thought she might have photosensitive epilepsy
like her twin sister. Anticonvulsant treatment was discussed with Jennifer
and her mother. It was felt that we should wait for the result of the EEG
before considering anticonvulsants, if at all.

Jennifer's should only use computers with non-glare, non-flicker monitors in a well lighted rooms. She should sit at least 6 feet from the TV set and should avoid flickering lights and Discos.

Jennifer will be reviewed in 6 weeks time.

Yours sincerely

J Walker

Joseph Walker
SpR to Dr Hertz

Dr Walker has written a letter that:
• clearly identifies the patient by hospital number, names and address

• highlights the problem (the reason for the consultation- Convulsions while working on a computer)

• highlights investigation planned or done (EEG, CT head)

• summarises the history (convulsion while on computer, witnessed by teacher, period of sleep and then drowsiness)

• summarises past personal and family medical history (no past fits, twin sister treated for photosensitive epilepsy)

• states results of physical exam (growth, BP and CNS)

• states suspected diagnosis (photosensitive epilepsy like her twin)

• states issues discussed (mother agreed to wait for EEG result before decision on anticonvulsants; use computers with non-glare monitors; sit at least 6 feet from the TV and avoid flickering lights and Discos.

• states follow-up plans (Jennifer will be reviewed in 6 weeks time).

Jubilee Surgery
Duke Way,
Brambleton M76 3EF

23 June 2002

Dr Mark Gregory
Consultant Paediatrician
Brambleton General Hospital
Brambleton M75 9FT

Dear Dr Gregory

Re: Imran Mohamed Khalifar (d.o.b 23-5- 1999)
    34 Duke Way, Brambleton M76 3EF

Please see this lad who has had a cough for 3 years. He is not
responding to asthma inhalers. I had to give him oral steroid
recently. His mother brought him back saying his was much better
after the oral steroids given 2 weeks ago.

Yours sincerely
MBramble
Mary Bramble
GP registrar to Dr K. Shah

Dr Shah discussed the letter with his trainee on the weekly training session.
He pointed out that referral letter should informative:
* medication, doses and frequency of use should have been included
* how the inhalers were used in a 3 year old should be indicated
* the letter implies that the child should be given regular oral steroids
* it is not clear what advice Dr Bramble is seeking.

Dr Shah requested Dr Bramble to reflect on her referral letter and to revise
it. The registrar rewrote the letter that afternoon.

Jubilee Surgery
Duke Way,
Brambleton M76 3EF

25 June 2002

Dr Mark Gregory
Consultant Paediatrician
Brambleton General Hospital
Brambleton M75 9FT

Dear Dr Gregory

Re: Imran Mohamed Khalifar (d.o.b 23-5- 1999)
34 Duke Way, Brambleton M76 3EF

Would you please see Imran, a 3 year old with a chronic cough and advise.
He is not responding to Ventolin 2 puffs via Volumatic for asthma.

Two weeks ago he was given a 3 day course of oral steroids because his cough
was worse and he wheezed.

He was back yesterday with cough and wheeze worse on playing with
siblings. His mother said the asthma was much better after the oral steroids.

Imran's father and uncle use Becotide inhalers for asthma. Is it safe to give
a 3 year old long term inhaled steroids?

Yours sincerely
M Bramble
Mary Bramble
GP registrar to Dr K. Shah

Brambleton General Hospital
Brambleton M75 9FT

Our Ref Z0486579

23 June 2002

Mr Robert Staples
Consultant Surgeon
Brambleton General Hospital
Brambleton M75 9FT.

Dear Mr Staples

Re: Daniel McFee (born 12.07.1991)
56 Zender Close, Brambleton M76 9QL.

Problem: Enlarged firm lymph node mass in neck.

Request: Evaluation with a view to an excision biopsy.

Donald has a large gland (each 4cm diameter) on the left side of his neck.
It was noted 6 weeks ago and is getting bigger. He has night fevers and has
lost 3 kg in weight in the last 4 weeks.

A sister had tuberculosis 5 years ago. Daniel's chest X-ray was normal;
and two tuberculin tests were negative.

Is the gland neoplastic?

Regards,

MGregory

Dr Mark Gregory MD FRCPCH
Consultant Paediatrician

cc. Dr Kamran Shah, Jubilee Surgery, Duke Way, Brambleton M76 3EF

9.6.6 Letter to a parent

Brambleton General Hospital
Brambleton M75 9FT

Our Ref: X4534652

23 May 2002

Mrs Fiona McDonald
45 Nottingham Close
Brambleton M76 8QL.

Dear Mrs McDonald

Re: Donald's medicine to prevent urine infection
This is to inform you that scan of Donald's kidneys shows that the left ureter (a tube taking urine from the kidney to the bladder) is still dilated.

We need to find out why this is so. I have asked Dr Peters, our Consultant Radiologist, to do some special scans of Donald's urinary system.

Could we meet in my clinic next Wednesday 5th June 2002, at 11 am to discuss the ultrasound scan report and the additional scans?

Please continue with trimethoprim at night to prevent a water infection.

Please ring me at the hospital if you would like to discuss this further.

Yours sincerely

M Gregory

Mark Gregory MD FRCPCH
Consultant Paediatrician

cc: Dr J Williams, Moss Surgery, Moss Lane, Catsford M76 4ZP

Letters to patients or parents (in paediatrics) are sometimes long than those to the GP on the same problem. They are more difficult to write well.

Medical information must be conveyed accurately without technical jargon. Some letter-writers add subheadings to sections of their letters. Others arrange the material with headings in mind but do not include them in the text. In the *'Hospital discharge summary',* subheadings are used; but the *'Outpatient clinic letter'* omits them.

9.7. Clinical Reports

Commissioned reports have terms of reference- the nature of the investigation (area of concern/interest), its scope and limitations. These govern the detail of the report and its recommendations.

9.7.1 What is a clinical report?

A clinical report is a document written to communicate clinical findings and recommendations about a clinical problem, incident or phenomenon to a person or people with a legitimate interest in the subject.

Before writing a report you should have a clear understanding of:
• the purpose of the report
• the audience (who it is aimed at)
• who will read it and who will use it
• what you want to communicate, achieve, how and why?

Think about the audience. What is their:
• authority (ability to act on the report)?
• knowledge of the subject (*to judge the pitch of the report*)?
• level of education (*to decide appropriate language*)?
• attitude towards the subject (*biases you must overcome*)?

The majority of clinical reports (clinical audits, hospital incidents and case reports for police or social services are relatively easy to write. However when responding to a complaint about clinical care, the report must be written much more carefully. Your report could be used in legal proceedings against you or your hospital. Read the lawyer's instructing letter; review the patient's complaint before responding.

9.7.2 Structure of a report

A report has a structure- a beginning, a body and an end:
• an introduction to say what the report is about

- the body to tell readers what you want them to know
- a summary to state the essence of the report.

Published reports have a standard structure- what readers expect to find when they open a *report*. If your report departs too far from this structure, the unusual format may reduce the impact of your findings and recommendations.

Some reports are so brief, a page or two, that the normal structure is condensed. However you should write them with the same headings in mind. A few headings, like title page, contents list and appendices, may be omitted in short reports. Some will be expressed in one or two paragraphs.

A long report is organised in sections: title page, contents list, summary, an introduction, body of the report, conclusions, recommendations, references (bibliography) and appendices.

Title page shows:
- the title (official name of the report)
- the author(s') name(s)
- a statement of the subject of the report
- the date (of writing or publication).

The Contents list shows the full list of sections or chapters of the report (including appendices, references, etc) and their page numbers.

The Summary should concisely outline the report in two or three short paragraphs. The summary is usually written last, and in the third person singular.

> *"This report considered the use of herbal remedies in post-term pregnancies."*

The ***Introduction*** gives a concise explanation of the terms (aims/context) of the report. It should contain brief details of essential background information to enable the reader to understand the subject of inquiry and its findings and recommendations.

The body of the report is where you write the main findings of the case, audit or inquiry. It should:

- be based on an analysis of the issues and findings
- support what is written with evidence and argument
- make a clear distinction between facts and opinions.

The body should be subdivided into sections (or chapters) if the report is long. Sections should be sequentially numbered *(as in this book)* to assist reference to material. Graphs and charts should be used where and when appropriate.

Conclusions are the judgements (opinions) you have reached after studying the subject:
> *"The poor clinical outcomes were caused by shortage of resources and not poor clinical skills or lack of effort."*

Conclusions should not be confused with recommendations.

Recommendations are the actions your conclusions lead you to believe are necessary to improve the situation:
> *"All new midwives and paediatric staff should be taught neonatal resuscitation."*

The *references* *(bibliography)* section gives details of sources cited in the report. Use the format of the '*International Committee of Medical Journal Editors*' for citing references. Example:

1. Jain A, Ogden J. **General practitioners' experiences of patients' complaints: qualitative study.** *BMJ* 1999; 318:1596-1599

2. Goleman D. **Working with emotional intelligence.** London: Bloomsbury 1998

Appendices
This is the place where information not essential to the flow of the argument of the report, but which some readers may wish to study, is placed.

Summary

- Clinical notes and letters are legal documents with legal implications. They legally belong to the Secretary of State for Health. The patient has a legal right to see her notes and to receive copies.

- Every entry into case notes should have the dated and time of writing. The writer should sign and printed her/his name.

- The record or message should be as clear, concise and simple as possible using short words and paragraphs.

- Clinical documents record clinical activity or event in notes so that they can be consulted later or to pass on information

- The aim of a clinical letter is to transmit or seek information or advice (consultation) or practical assistance (referral).

- The letter must give the identity, clinical problems or diagnosis, state the treatments with adequate details to enable future modification.

- A clinical report communicates clinical findings about a clinical problem, incident or phenomenon to people with a legitimate interest in the subject and may recommend a remedy or action.

- Reports have a standard structure; an unusual format may reduce the impact of the findings and/or recommendations.

- Only sign documents whose content you are happy with.

Reading

1. Mort S. **Professional Report Writing.** London: Cower 1995.

2. Peel M. **Improving Your Communication Skills.** London: Kogan Page 1995.

3. International Committee of Medical Journal Editors. **Uniform Requirements for Manuscripts submitted to Biomedical Journals.** *Ann Intern Med.* 1997; 126: 36-47.

10 Medico-legal reports

10.1 Reports of legal interest

On page 135 is a fictitious report on a teenager who was injured in a road traffic accident. The report on page 137 describes the findings in an infant who might have been deliberately injured (*non-accidental injury or NAI*).

You will, in your medical career, be asked (instructed) by lawyers, police or social workers for reports on patients you have seen. A & E doctors are frequently asked for reports on patients they have treated. Paediatric registrars are encouraged to write reports (under supervision) on children they have examined for suspected NAI.

SHO are not normally expected to write medico-legal reports. However SHOs in A&E are often called to courts to give evidence on patients they have treated.

The examples have been written by consultants and convey the essentials elements of medico-legal reporting.

Registrars and doctors working at registrar level write medical legal reports under supervision from the consultant in charge of the patient.

When writing medico-legal reports (for social services, police and lawyers) remember that your report may be used in a court of law and you may be cross-examine on its contents. So:

• State your names, qualification and appointment and experience and in which capacity you saw the patient.

• Explain why you are an expert in the field. Do not claim an expertise you do not have. Don't let your emotions affect the tone of your report. Do not include anything that you would not repeat under oath.

• The report will be read by people with minimal medical knowledge. Use short words, short phrases and short paragraphs. Avoid or explain unavoidable medical jargon. Describe events sequentially so that the flow of the report is clear and logical.

- Name (list) all sources of the evidence you used to reach your diagnosis and conclusions, however insignificant or trivial it may seem. List documents your read or used, telephone conversations, and face to face interviews (give names of people you talked to in your evaluation of the case).

- List the investigations you used to obtain information and to a make the diagnosis (history, physical examination, measurements of lesions (bruises, abrasions, lacerations, tears, etc,) laboratory tests, X-rays and scans, sizes of skulls fractures, photographs (essential in skin like bruises and tears, swelling, etc.).

- Separate facts from their interpretation. Keep matters of fact separate from matters of opinion. Separate interpretation from conclusions.

- Summarise your findings and opinion at the beginning of the report.
- Give a list of references (books and journal articles, reports) that back up your views on the case, the evidence for your conclusions.

- Number the pages and use the patient's name as a footer. If the report is long, include a title page, a contents list and a summary.

- Sign and date the report.

Example 1: *Road traffic accident causing fracture of femur.*
Solicitors (lawyers) representing a passenger in one of the vehicle involved in the accident have asked the orthopaedic surgeon for a report on the injuries, their treatment and prognosis.

Example 2. *A baby has been brought to A&E with an unexplained injury.*
An A&E doctor examined the child, arranged an X-ray of the injured limb and informed paediatricians of her concerns about the cause of the injury. The registrar in-turn informed the consultant paediatrician on call. The boy was admitted and social services informed about the boy and his injury.

Report on a bone fracture from a road traffic accident

Department of Orthopedics
Brambleton General Hospital
Brambleton M75 9FT

Our Ref: Z0686983

23 July 2002

Miss Kate Nightingale
Nightingales and Swift Solicitors
Rample Avenue
Catsford M75 2GF.

Dear Miss Nightingale

**Re: Simon Redwood (d o b 22.06.1986)
    12 Duke Way, Catsford M75 2JF.**

Subject: Fracture of right femur

I, Kevin Moynihan, MB ChB FRCS, employed as consultant orthopaedic
surgeon at Catsford General Hospital, examined Simon Redwood in the
Accident and Emergency (A&E) of the hospital at 10 a.m. on 21 July 2002.
He was brought to A&E by ambulance from the scene of a road traffic
accident..

The skin over the fracture point had an oval bruise of about 5 cm in diameter,
but intact. There was faint superficial bruising over the right knee of about 6
cm wide (across the knee cap and about 4 cm wide. His right thigh bone
(femur) was completely fractured (broken) at about one foot above the knee.

Mr Redwood's fracture was reduced and fixed with a metal rod inserted into
the bone shaft.

He was discharged home two days later. He will need a crutch weight so that he does no put weight on his right leg for six weeks.

Mr Redwood will be followed in my clinic of this hospital.

Full recovery is expected.

Yours sincerely

KMoynihan

Kevin Moynihan MB ChB FRCS
Consultant Orthopedic Surgeon

Copy: Dr R. Peters, Jubilee Surgery, Duke Way, Catsford

Report on a suspected a non-accidental injury (to social services)

Department of Child Health
Brambleton General Hospital
Brambleton M75 9FT

Our Ref: Z0486582

23 July 2002

Mrs Kate Simpkin
Child protection unit
Catsford Social Services
Catsford M75 2GF.

Dear Mrs Nightingale

Re: Jamie Redwood (d o b 23.11.2001)
12 Duke Way, Catsford M75 2JF.

Subject: Spiral fracture of the left humerus (upper arm bone)
I, Dr Michael Smith MB MD FRCPCH, consultant paediatrician at
Catsford General Hospital, examined Jamie in the Accident and
Emergency (A&E) of the hospital at 10 a.m. on 21 July 2002.

Jamie Redwood was brought to (A&E) by his mother, Sara Redwood and
his maternal grand mother, Mrs Diana Redwood. Diana Redwood told me
that she had arrived at her daughter's flat at 08.30 and found her grandson
quiet and miserable. She said Jamie had cried when she lifted him from his
pram. She said she had noticed that Jamie's left arm was swollen.

Diana Redwood told me she had been told her daughter that Jamie had fallen
off a chair onto the floor at while playing with Leroy, Sarah's boyfriend.
Sarah cried when I asked her to tell me what had caused Jamie's injury.

Jamie was well nourished and clean. He related well to his mother and grandmother. There were no bruises or scars. His weight was 8.8kg (50th centile), length was 72cm (75th centile), head circumference was 46 cm (50th centile. His size was normal for his age.

The upper part of his left arm was swollen and painful to touch.

An X-ray showed a spiral fracture of the humerus (upper arm bone). A skeletal survey (X-ray of all his bone) found healing fractures of the right 5th and 6th ribs.

Causes for concern
1. The boy's arm was swollen and painful. Delay in seeking medical advice was suspicious.

2. Spiral fracturing requires a twisting force.

3. Falling downstairs is unlikely to cause a spiral fracture of the humerus in an 8 months old baby.

4. Jamie had unexplained rib fractures.

Opinion: The explanation given for Jamie's fracture of the left upper arm bone (humerus) is not consistent with the injuries found. The recent fracture of the humerus and the healing fractures of ribs were unlikely to be accidental.

Yours faithfully

MSmith
Michael Smith MB ChB MD FRCPCH
Consultant Paediatrician

Copy: Dr R. Peters, Jubilee Surgery, Duke Way, Catsford M76 3EF

10.2 Responding to complaints
Letters of complaint are usually addressed to the chief executive (CEO) of trusts (hospital and primary care). Patients may however write to any

senior member of the trust (chairman, board directors, a senior doctor or nurse, a senior therapist or a manager). Such complaints are processed through one office (the complaint office or the public relations office).

10.2.1 Processing written complains
Usually:
- the CEO requests the Public Relations Officer (PRO) to handle the complaint (*contact named individual(s) and others and get their response*)

- the PRO writes to individual(s) cited by the complaint to explain themselves

- the individual(s) cited respond in writing to the PRO (*they present their views on the allegations made in the complaint*)

- the PRO may seek comments from other individuals present at the incident to clarify issues (*other trust staff may have witnessed or been involved in the incident from which the complaint arose*)

- the PRO drafts a letter (for the CEO) replying to the complaint (*chief executives can not personally investigate and respond to every thing)*

- the individual(s) cited must see the draft letter (*it is good practice for PRO to show the draft response to the doctor complained about. If the doctor disagrees then they could discuss the issue*).

- the CEO reads the letter and if it is satisfactory, signs it. The official response is the sent to the complainant.

Most complainants are satisfied by the chief executive's reply. However some are not happy with the reply and may contact their MP or consult lawyers with a view to suing the trust and the doctor.

10.2.2 Preparing a response
Before (putting pen to paper or fingers to keyboard) carefully read the complaint again. What is the complaint about? Try and recall the incident leading to the complaint. Make notes of your recollections. Discuss the complaint with you consultant, with an informed and trusted colleague or

better still with the MDU or MPS.

Respond only to issues raised in the complaint. Do not open new topics. Do not mention difficulties you might have had with the patient in the past. Your should only respond to issues (all of them) cited in the complaint.

If matters seem serious, if you know they are serious, consult your medical protection organisation (MDU, MPS or other) immediately and inform the trust's legal unit. Do not alter (erase, remove or add to, or otherwise change the patient's notes; experts can tell if you do). Speak to your consultant. Discuss the problem with a trusted friend.

10.3 Handling press interest
If the press gets involved, ***do not discuss the subject with reporters*** (newspaper TV, radio or any other reporter). ***Not even off record***. Nothing is off record for a reporter. The complainant has the freedom to talk to the press. You do not. Maintain patient confidentiality. Leave communicating with the press to the trust's public relations officer.

10.4 GMC's *Confidentiality: Protecting and Providing Information*

Section 1 - Patients' right to confidentiality
1. Patients have a right to expect that information about them will be held in confidence by their doctors. Confidentiality is central to trust between doctors and patients. Without assurances about confidentiality, patients may be reluctant to give doctors the information they need in order to provide good care. If you are asked to provide information about patients you should:

   a. Seek patients' consent to disclosure of information wherever possible, whether or not you judge that patients can be identified from the disclosure.
   b. Anonymise data where unidentifiable data will serve the purpose.
   c. Keep disclosures to the minimum necessary. You must always be prepared to justify your decisions in accordance with this guidance.

Protecting information

2. When you are responsible for personal information about patients you must make sure that it is effectively protected against improper disclosure at all times.

3. Many improper disclosures are unintentional. You should not discuss patients where you can be overheard or leave patients' records, either on paper or on screen, where they can be seen by other patients, unauthorised health care staff or the public. Whenever possible you should take steps to ensure that your consultations with patients are private.

Summary

- If a patient complains about you, seek advice from your consultant. If the matter is serious consult the MDU or the MPS right away.

- When writing medico-legal reports:
  - keep as objective as possible
  - do not claim an expertise you do not have
  - separate facts from their interpretation
  - separate interpretation from conclusions
  - distinguish the probable from the possible, and
  - cite sources of evidence for your conclusions.

- Do not discuss clinical complaints with the press- not even off record. Maintain patient confidentiality.

- Only sign documents whose content you are happy with.

Further Reading

1. Mort S. **Professional Report Writing.** Cower 1995.

2. Jain A, Ogden J. **General practitioners' experiences of patients' complaints: qualitative study.** *BMJ* 1999; 318: 1596-1599

3. Suresh K. **Writing a medico-legal report.** *BMJ* 2002; 325: s111

4. GMC. **Confidentiality: Protecting and Providing Information**. September 2000.

11. Clinical Audit

11.1 What is clinical audit?

To **audit** means to account for, to balance, check, examine, to verify something against expectations, what should have been done.

Clinical audit = checking that past clinical activity went as planned, was done as expected. Clinical activities are audited, scrutinized or compared with expectations, with standards.

Clinical audit is not research. It is easy to confuse clinical *audit* with clinical *research*. Similar, if not identical, tools are employed in performing and communicating either.

In clinical audit what should be done, how when and the level of performance are known or assumed. A set yardstick or standard is used to measure performance. The auditor checks to see if a clinical practice followed a set standard.

[*Standard* = level, degree, excellence; benchmark, specification, measure, guide; flag, banner, pennant, etc.].

Research (re-search) means *searching again* for an insight, an answer to an intriguing question or problem. The research must find answers to *what, how, when, who/whom* before guideline or standards can be established.

Good clinical audits may point to important clinical questions. Why are the guidelines not followed? Why is the performance so poor?

11.2 Who needs clinical audit?

Clinical audit is useful to the clinician and the organisation (hospital, trust or clinic) he/she works in. Clinical audit:
- enables the individual or organisation to systematically examine performance and/or outcomes in relation to the expected (standards)

- helps the clinician or the service to identify deficiencies in performance and resources, to identify deficits and provides evidence of what should be changed/ modified, encouraged or terminated

- facilitates the collection of evidence on which change in standards, practices and provision of resources may be based.

11.3 Audit standards

Clinical audit involves making judgments (satisfactory, better or worse). Judging requires comparison with expected practice, expected outcomes or against established norms. So standards or comparators are necessary. If they are not available they are empirically set and adjusted with experience.

Where do standards come from?

Initially performance at leading hospitals sets the standards for:
- *clinical issues:* diagnosis, treatment, survival, complication rates, etc.
- *managerial issues:* staffing needs, service costs, utilisation rates, etc.

Retrospective studies have provided data for setting preliminary standards. *Pilot studies* may be necessary to try out new practices before the norms, before the standard can be gauged.

Monitoring current practice and ironing out problems may lead to better outcomes. The new practices and outcomes then become standards against which future performance is judged.

11.4 Examples of clinical audit

- Clinical decisions (diagnosis, treatments, conformity to guidelines, prescription habits, etc.)

- Clinical outcomes (survival, re-admissions, complications) after some intervention

- Managerial issues (waiting times, turnover, hospital stay, cost per unit of activity, etc.).

- Complaints (causes, response, resolution, complaint rates, etc.).

11.5 Sources of information

Data for clinical audit can be gathered from many sources. The following are used most often:

- *clinical notes* (paper and computer based)
- *questionnaires* for clinicians, patients and/or relatives, managers, etc.
- *pathology records* (tissue analysis- sampled in life or postmortem)
- *managerial records* (financial, absence record, staff turnover, etc.)
- *patient complaints* (causes, response, resolution, complaint rates, etc.)
- *published material* (medical press, local publications, trust reports, reports from/about peer organisations, etc.).

11.6 Requirements for clinical audit

Informative audits are not cheap. They require time, money, people and the will to do them well. Small audits are useful as training tools for novices, but should not be used to determine major changes in practice.

An informative clinical audit needs:
- An intriguing / important problem to audit
- An intrigued / challenged mind to supervise or perform the audit
- Integrity/ skill in making judgements on disorganised data
- Resources (people, materials, money, time, space) for the audit.

11.7 Clinical auditing

Novices underestimate the time and tedium involved in doing audits:
- culling information from case note can be frustrating (missing notes, missing data, scattered reports, illegibility, notes wanted elsewhere).

- data from large organization may take time to obtain because of lack of urgency or concerns about *security* and *confidentiality*.

- interviewing people is expensive in time and human resources (time from regular work for the auditor or hiring assistants).

- informative *questionnaires* are *difficult to design* (for reliability and relevancy) and may not be completed by the *relevant subjects*.

Start early and get on with it.

11.8 Analysing audit data

Most audits do not require complicated statistical analysis. Simple tabulations and calculation of percentages is usually enough.

A neglected aspect of audit is *qualitative* analysis for causes of good, superior or poor performance. Why are things this bad or so good? Most audits stress how much the performance differs from the expected, but not why.

The amount (quantity) of difference and its importance (significance) are determined by **quantitative** analysis. Quantitative (*statistical analysis*) tries to determine the **statistical significance** of the observed differences. Did the difference noted come about by chance?

Why is essential for **qualitative** analysis, to understanding the reason behind what is observed. Why is the performance so poor, good, so outstanding? Understanding the causes of poor, acceptable or outstanding performance is essential to improving the service or activity. Without the **why**, there is neither a rationale for change no **how** to change.

11.9 Writing the audit report

The subject is *introduced*, *methods* described, *results* revealed and *discussed* in relation to previous audits or studies in the area. The discussion should point out how the audit could have been done better.

Audit reports follow the standard format for scientific papers, IMRD. IMRD = Introduction, Methods, Results, and Discussion.

Conclusions based on the audit are drawn and *Recommendations* to remedy or correct identified flaws are made. Recommendations should be sensible and practical.

Before its release the report should acquire a **title** on a **title page**, a **summary**, a listing of the **contents**, a list of **references** and often, an **appendix.**

11.9.1 Title page

This page should display, in an attractive format the following only:

- the title (the name of the report)
- author(s) names
- a statement on the subject of the report
- the date (of writing or publication).

The title should be short, pithy and should embody the essence of the audit. Examples:
- Reduction in cancelled clinic appointments
- Survival after hip replacement in the elderly
- Time to administration of streptokinase after myocardial infarction.

11.9.2 Summary
The summary (abstract) should be short, succinct and should crystallise the findings of the audit. It is usually written after the body of the report is finished. It is then placed at the beginning of the report- just after the title page. The summary is called an *executive summary* in official reports. Is it the only part of the report executives read?

11.9.3 Introduction
The introduction gives reasons for doing the audit. **Why** and **what** was done are explained. The current situation or practice is described to introduce the issue(s) to the reader.

11.9.4 Methods
Methods (methodology) describe *what* was done and *how* it was done. *What* did you do? *How* did you do it? Answers to these questions should be laid out in the report. Statistical methods and software packages used should be named.

11.9.5 Results
What did you find? The findings of your audit should be clearly described. Give enough detail (tables, figures, quotes) to convey the results of the

audit. State and describe the results only. Do not comment on their importance or meaning- that will be done in the discussion. If some material is long or complex, put it in the appendix.

11.9.6 Discussion
The discussion covers and attempts to answer, the following questions.

- What do the findings mean?
- How do they compare with previous audits?
- Could you have done it better? How?

11.9.7 Conclusions
- What did you conclude from the audit?
- What are the implications of your audit?

11.9.8 Recommendations
Recommendations state what should be done to maintain (satisfactory situation), improve (unsatisfactory state) or disseminate (excellent) practice). Sometimes an audit leads to closure of a service or an activity.

11.9.9 References
The reference (bibliography) section lists all the sources quoted and the standards you have used .

11.9.10 Appendices.
This is the place for material not essential to the flow of the argument of the report, but which some readers may wish to study.

11.10 Closing the audit cycle
The recommendations of the audit should, if the authorities wish, be implemented. The cycle is closed after the recommendations have been implemented, taken root and the reformed service or activity has been re-audited. The cycle then continues.

Recommendations should be followed by a brief comment about the need and timing of a re-audit. The re-audit occurs after recommendations have been implemented. This *audit- reform- audit* process is called *the audit cycle (loop).*

Summary

- *Clinical audit* = checking (judging) that past clinical activity went as as expected, met standards

- Judgment requires comparison with standards or comparators

- Standard come from published reports, pilot projects, trial and error or are set empirically (guess work)

- Good audits result from deployment of resources (time, money, people) and the will to do a good job

- Quantitative and qualitative analyses are essential to explaining the magnitude of the deference, why it exists and how to respond

- The audit report should be written under headings: **I**ntroduction, **M**ethods, **R**esults, **D**iscussion, **C**onclusions and **R**ecommendations

- Before it is released, the report acquires a *title* on a *title page*, a *summary*, a list *contents*, a list of *references* and often *appendices*..

Further Reading

1. *Mort* S. **Professional Report Writing.** *Cower* 1995

2. NeLH Team. **Principles for Best Practice in Clinical Audit.** Radcliffe Medical Press Ltd 2002.

---

12. Research and publish

12.1. What is research?

The word research has fallen in status. What should be basic reading, search for information is now called research. Dictionaries suggest that *search* is now more rigorous than *research*.

To me *research* (re-search) means *search again* for an insight, an answer, a solution, to an intriguing question or problem. It is more than a basic library *search* (reading books, journals or magazines) on the subject.

Accessible information should be gathered in order to clarify, to refine the question for *searching again*- research. Often the answer to what initially looked difficult is found in published texts or on the internet. To re-search you should have searched before. Semantics aside, why should you be involved in research?

12.2 Why 'do research'?

Not every SHO or registrar will do research or write theses for higher degrees. Research is discussed here to give you an idea of what is expected *if* and *when* the opportunity arises.

Good research is rewarding to the individual and society. The public benefits from the fruits of research- telecommunications, engineering, physics, medicine, etc.

For most clinicians research involves looking for answers to clinical problems. Published authors are well regarded by their colleagues. They make presentations at scientific meetings, publish articles in journals and chapters in learned books. They cite their publications in their CVs.

Doing research gives you the opportunity to learn the science of medical inquiry and the opportunity to enhance your CV.

12.3 Requirements for research

Research is not cheap. It requires:
* An intriguing / important problem to solve
* An intrigued / challenged mind to supervise or perform the research
* Intelligence/ skill/ integrity in making judgments
* Resources (people, material, money, time, space, advice and support).

12.3.1 Urge to research

The two most import prerequisites for good research are an intriguing or challenging problem and an intrigued, challenged and competent mind.

Without the challenges it is difficult to sustain a research effort. The desire to solve a problem helps in looking for time, space and money (personal savings, grants from individuals and public bodies).

12.3.2 Money for research

Money to support research may come from personal savings. However increasingly, major research is becoming too expensive for ordinary people to fund from private means. It needs big money and that comes from government supported research organisations, research foundations, big business or occasionally rich philanthropists.

Getting money for research involves writing research proposals and applying for grants. If you intend to get involved in serious research you should:
* talk to professional researchers for career advice
* learn how to write winning research proposals
* find sources research funding for your specialty
* learn to handle interviews for research grants.

12.4 Planning Research

Many students and young doctors, ask for help in doing research before they have identified the intriguing / important problem they wish to pursue.

James Mitchell had always been interested in research. However he had not secured a research registrar post. He mentioned his interest during his initial interview with Dr Judith Watson, the clinical tutor in paediatrics at Catsford General Hospital..

"Which area of paediatrics would you like to research?"

"I am interested in atypical pneumonia.. What proportion of paediatric pneumonia is caused by mycoplasma?" James replied.

"What is the importance of knowing the incidence of mycoplasma pneumonia?" Dr Smith probed.

"If we knew the incidence of mycoplasma pneumoniae pneumonia we would have a good reason for requesting mycoplasma serology and treating with erythromycin or its newer relatives for at least 10 days" James replied. He was informed about the subject t.

"That might be an interesting piece of research. Think about how you would go about it- approvals, collaborators, funding, et cetera. We can discuss it again in 2 weeks, after the Thursday morning ward round."

Planning research means more than getting ideas. What should be done depends on the research project. Research on **humans** and **animals** *requires* **approval** from control bodies.

Studies involving **human** subjects require **informed consent** from the individuals or somebody acting for them **before** the research can start.

In the UK as in most developed countries clinical research can only proceed **after approval** from a **'Research Ethics Committee'** and the NHS Trust's **Research and Development Committee**.

The process can be protracted and permission may be denied without apparent good reason. The prime concern of Ethics Committees is to ensure patient safety. Important concerns of Ethics Committees include:
• Is the research likely to be clinically important to society?
• Is it primary research or a repetition of other peoples' work?
• How will the patient's welfare be protected?

Before starting on any research you must have approval from the Research and Development Committee of your NHS Trust in which the patients involved in the study would be treated. The trust needs to be satisfied that patient safety will not be compromised. It may also provide human and financial support for the project.

If you are interested in clinical research, you should find out where and when the local Ethics Committee meets and the membership. Get a copy of the committee's research guidelines and study them before committing yourself to a piece of research.

12.5. Doing research

Details of research are beyond the remit of this book. The local university library should have books on medical research. Some of your consultants should be able to point you in the right direction.

Does your research require:

- laboratory experiments (permits, equipment, materials, assistants...)?
- human subjects (informed consent, approval by Ethics Committee...)?
- interviewing people (questionnaires, assistants...)?

These and many other issues must be considered and solved before the study begins. Politeness and humility are essential in medical and sociological research. *"Please"* and *"thank you"* are essential tools.

James obtained and read research guidelines from the local ethical committee. After discussing them with Dr Smith he decided not attempt a prospective study:

- *he did not have access to laboratory resources. The local laboratory was not able to help with serology for mycoplasma on many children with respiratory symptom*

- *he did not have the human resources to organise parental/patient consent to participate in the research, no to collect blood samples from children whose parents agreed*

The laboratory allowed his to use its database for a retrospective study of the incidence f mycoplasma pneumoniae infection in children starting from requests for respiratory pathogen serology in children.

After appropriate approvals, he traced and read case notes of children whose serum had elevated anti-mycoplasma IgM. From the notes he extracted details of clinical presentation, time to diagnosis, radiological findings, antibiotics prescribed, duration of therapy and outpatient follow up.

12.6 Analysing data

James' retrospective study was descriptive and required no statistical analysis. He calculated the proportion of paediatric requests for respiratory serology that were positive for mycoplasma IgM. He could not draw any conclusions from the clinical details and serological studies because:

- *few clinical symptoms and signs were recorded in the notes*
- *he could not determine whether serology was requested in all children with typical symptoms and signs*
- *details of antibiotic prescription were incomplete*
- *not all children with symptoms suggestive of mycoplasma pneumonia were followed up as outpatients*

He wrote up his findings and presented them at departmental meeting on Research and Audit. His clinical tutor agreed with him that the study was not good enough for submission to a journal for publication.

From the discussion of his presentation the department agreed that:

- *important clinical details should be written into the case notes*
- *reasons for requesting laboratory test should always be recorded*
- *indications, names and dosage of drugs and duration of therapy should be recorded in the case notes, discharge and outpatient letters.*

Although James did not prospectively study the incidence of mycoplasma pneumonia in children the retrospective study was useful:

- *it demonstrated the kind of problems a single clinician faces when he/she attempts to do research without adequate support*
- *it was used as a basis for discussing the adequacy of clinical notes, prescribing of antibiotics and the writing of clinical letters.*

Some research findings are easy to quantify and others are not. Most socio-medical studies are more interesting when their qualitative (flavour) as well as quantitative trends are reported. The style of analysis and reporting depends on the primary question.

12.7 Writing the paper

Research papers usually follow a standard format: *Introduction, Methods, Results, Discussion (IMRD), plus Conclusion and*

Recommendations. Study published journal articles in your library.

Important discoveries have, however, been reported in letters to editors of journals. The structure of deoxyribonucleic acid (DNA), the genetic code, was reported by Watson and Crick in a letter to *The Lancet,* a British medical journal.

12.7.1 The title of the paper
The title should encapsulate the subject and findings of the study. It should be short, relevant, informative, and memorable. *Incidence of childhood mycoplasma pneumonia* would be nice for Dr Mitchell's study.

12.7.2 Abstract
Although it follows the title, the abstract (summary) is written last. It gives a summary of the purpose, methods, findings and conclusions of the study. It should capture the essence of the paper.

Mycoplasma pneumonia in children admitted to Catsford General Hospital (July 1999- June 2002). James Mitchell, Specialist Registrar in Paediatrics, Catsford General Hospital.

ABSTRACT
Objective: To determine the incidence of mycoplasma pneumonia in children hospitalised with pneumonia.

Subjects and methods. The number of requests for respiratory pathogen serology and the identity of children with raised mycoplasma IgM titres were identified from the microbiology laboratory data base. Case notes were scrutinised for clinical and radiological information.

Findings: Only 5 of 98 sera tested (5.1%) had raised mycoplasma IgM. Clinical details were too scanty to build a picture of mycoplasma pneumonia.

Conclusion: The retrospective study did not find enough clinical detail to determine the incidence of mycoplasma pneumonia in hospitalised children..

Abstracts are written in different formats. Sometimes subheadings are omitted and the abstract merges into a solid paragraph. I prefer those with subheadings. They are easier to read. Many doctors read the abstract and only when the article is interesting or relevant to their practice do they study it in detail.

12.7.3 Introduction
Why was the study done?
What were you looking for?

James was intrigued by the morbidity associated with mycoplasma pneumonia and wanted to know the incidence.

12.7.4 Methods (including subjects and materials)
• What did you study (subjects)? *James studied the frequency of mycoplasma IgM in sera of children with respiratory symptoms.*

• What did you do? *He extracted information of serology for respiratory pathogens from the microbiology laboratory database.*

• How did you do it?
He counted the number of children whose sera were tested and identified those with raised mycoplasma pneumoniae IgM. Then he located case notes of children with high mycoplasma IgM and extracted clinical details.

12.7.5 Results (findings)
• What did you find?
As he did not know the incidence of mycoplasma pneumonia he could not decide if 5% was a low or high sero-positive rate.

Statistical analysis
Statistical analysis is important in serious research. It attempts to measure the probability (likelihood) that the differences observed occurred by came chance.

James' retrospective study very small. Statistical tests were not necessary. There was no data to test.

12.7.6 Discussion
What do the findings mean?

How do your findings compare with published studies?
Could you have done this study better? How?
James wished he could have done a prospective estimate of the incidence of mycoplasma pneumonia in children.

12.7.7 Conclusions
What are your conclusions?
What are the implications of your findings?

12.7.8 Recommendations
What should be done next?

12.7.9 References
At the end of a paper for publication, the author gives details of papers and books he has referred to in the article. References enable readers to search for, and read texts that have been quoted. Use the Vancouver format. Example:

Citing references

Citing a book:
Kohn LT, Corrigan JM, Donaldson MM, eds. *To err is human. Building a safer health system.* Washington, DC: National Academy Press, 1999.

Citing a journal article:
Tookey PA, Johnson C, Ades AE, Peckham CS. Racial differences in rubella immunity among pregnant women. *Public Health* 1998; 102: 57-62.

Citing a report:
Department of Health. *Report of the working group of refugee doctors and dentists.* London: Department of Health, 2000.

Citing information on the internet:
MedicalForum.com. Common interview questions. www.medicalforum.com/interview_qlist.html (accessed 19 Feb 2002)

Do not misquote the publication to give false support to your research. You risk being found out and disgraced in the same journal.

I have often wished that popular magazines would quote their sources. Often, I read something interesting in a magazine, want to follow it up, but can't. The source of the information was not given!

Summary

- Think careful about your research question. Is it intriguing and exciting?

- Identify resources (personal funds, research grants and time)

- Obtain approvals from relevant bodies (Home Office for animals studies Ethics Committee and Trust's Research and Development Committee for clinical research) before committing time and other resources.

- Plan your study with its analysis in mind; sample size, controls, inclusion and exclusion, etc. Have you asked "why, how, when" for insight into the qualitative aspect of your research?

- Analyse your data. What are the main findings of your study? Have you answered the primary question adequately?

- What were the deficits of the research? How would you correct them?

Find a publisher for your paper. Submit the dissertation to examiners.

Further Reading

1. Bowling A. **Research Methods in Health**. Oxford: Oxford University Press 2002

2. Campbell M. **Statistics at square one**. London: BMJ Books 2002

13. Dissertation/ thesis

13.1 Need for a higher degree

Perhaps you would like to enhance the impact of your CV by studying for and acquiring a higher university degree. Congratulations. You will miss a lot of TV, read a lot of waffle, and learn how to type (sorry, acquire keyboard skills!).

In pursuit of a higher university degree, may be an MSc, a ChM/ MS, an MD or a PhD, you will be required to write a dissertation or thesis. This will be scrutinised by university examiners. Some universities conduct oral examinations (viva voce) on dissertations and theses.

If your dissertation, like other requirements before it, is successful you will receive you degree. If unsuccessful you will have spent, maybe wasted the effort, money, time and labour, and missed much TV- but wiser.

13.2. What is a dissertation/thesis?

A dissertation (thesis) is an academic monograph prepared on the lines of a research paper, but much longer and thorough in exposition and detail. It is normally written at the behest of an academic institution for the requirements of a diploma or degree- MSc, MA, PhD or whatever.

Dissertation = critique, thesis, discourse, essay, exposition, treatise, etc.
Thesis = treatise, dissertation, essay, monograph, hypothesis, etc.

Discourses for Diplomas and some Master's degrees are usually called *dissertations,* while those for most Master's, MD and PhD degrees are called *theses.*

Now that you know the difference between *dissertation and thesis,* let us assume *dissertation = thesis* for the purposes of this chapter.

13.3 Supervisors

Preparing a dissertation for a higher degree begins with registration as a student of the university followed by assignment of a supervisor. Ideas for a dissertation are discussed with and guided by the supervisor.

Supervisors are particularly important for research based degrees. The supervisor decides if and when, the research and dissertation are progressing satisfactorily. He/she decides if and when the student may submit the dissertation to examiners and therefore if and when he will get the degree!

13.4 Length of a dissertation

It is the quality of your research, the detail and relevance of your data, the thoroughness of your analysis, the style and language of your writing that matter and not the weight *[pounds, kilograms]* of the *book*.

While a paper may be a few pages long, a dissertation is usually just under a hundred to a few hundred pages long. Some sections may be a few pages long, while others need division into chapters. The *Results* section is frequently a couple of chapters long. But a dissertation requires more than length.

A thesis is supposed to be more thorough than a dissertation. However some dissertations are quite good, better than some theses. Your university will have copies of successful theses/dissertations from past students for you to examine. Follow your university's requirements for diplomas and higher degrees. Get a copy of the guidelines for doing projects and writing of dissertations/theses early.

13.5 Structure of a dissertation

The structure of a dissertation is the same as that used for audits and research papers. The monograph is given a title on a title page, a summary, list of contents and completed with a list of references and an appendix.

* Title page (with the title of dissertation, author(s) names, a phrase specified by the institution and date of submission to examiners)
* A summary of the dissertation *(one to a few pages)*

- A list of contents and the pages they start on (*one to a few pages*)
- Introduction *(a number of pages)*
- Methods *(pages, may be a short chapter)*
- Results/findings *(a chapter or two)*
- Discussion *(pages to a chapter)*
- Conclusions (*a page or two*)
- Recommendations *(a page or two)*
- References (bibliography) *(one to several pages)*
- Appendices *(a number of pages)*.

If you are about to write a dissertation you should examine successful samples in your college or university library.

Study the dissertation for:
- structure and layout (format)
- the language (style and grammar)
- use of tables, figures and quotations
- depth and sophistication of exposition
- the *'finish'* (production) and quality of the *book*.

Select two you consider the best, study them closely and appreciate the attributes of a successful dissertation. When you write your own, do not copy the language of any particular thesis. Write it your way.

13.6 The tone of dissertation

What will be the tone of your dissertation? Many learned journals, reports and theses are written in the *third person singular*. It is claimed that this encourages objectivity.

- Third person singular:
- *The author studied the mating habits of 124 kites...*

- First person singular
  - *1 studied the mating habits of 124 kites...*

How the use of a phrase *"the author"* instead of the words "I" or "We", enhances objectivity? The claim to objectivity is false. One can be as biased in the *third* as in the *first person singular,* or plural for that matter.

The third person singular style produces clumsy prose. Repeating *"the author"* is tedious when a simple (and humble) *"I"* would suffice. Fortunately there is a welcome tendency to use the *I* or *We* voice in academic writing.

Find out what your examiners prefer and use that. After your diploma or degree you may write in whatever style you like.

13.7. Watch your language

Spelling and grammar may decide the outcome of you dissertation. If your story reads well, the spelling and grammar are correct, your examiners will be more likely to award marks more easily. Irritate them with poor spelling, grating grammatical mistakes and you make them mean (stingy).

Your dissertation should say what you want it to say; no more, no less
- think of what you want to say and how you will say it
- avoid ambiguity, your message should be clearly understood
- use clear simple words, avoid jargon wherever possible
- use short words, short sentences, and short paragraphs
- be methodical, tell the story sequentially
- avoid superfluous words and phrases
- avoid the urge to impress. Just write well.

Your thesis should be written in an active language. Emphasise the action of the methods, results, technical analysis *(with statistics if relevant)*, discussion and conclusion. This is when the first person singular is superior. Example:

1. I examined 234 mice

2. The author examined 234 mice

1. I measured serum zinc levels in 234 school children with the XS assay.

2. The author measured serum zinc levels in 234 school children with the XS chemical analysis system.

In the two examples above version (1) is short and precise, while (2) is longer and pompous.

13.8 Submitting dissertation to examiners

Universities have rules about preparing dissertations (general format, mandatory statements on the tittle page, word spacing and binding).

* Follow your university's rules.
* Follow your supervisor's advice about the academic quality of your dissertation

* Leave time for remedial work *(more* studies, analyses, literature reviews, rewrites, etc.)

* Sort out practical details (typing, binding, number of copies?) early

* Check the grammar- read what you have written. Spellcheckers still have difficulties with grammar.

When you and your tutor are happy with the dissertation, produce and submit the right number of copies for the examiners and wait. You can now read/write that novel or complete the clinical audit.

13.9 Defending your dissertation

Some universities examine candidates orally (viva voce) on their dissertations. In the Viva the candidate is questioned about her/his dissertation as part of the requirements for the degree. Usually there are at least two examiners *(inquisitors),* sometimes more.

Know your dissertation. Be ready to defend it in from attack by examiners. I have heard, that a long time ago in Europe, PhD candidates were examined in public. There, they defended their theses. If successful they were thereafter addressed as *'doctor'* Doctor originally meant learned person, teacher!

Be prepared to discuss the *why, how, what* and *when* of your dissertation
* why did you do the research/study?
* why did you do it that way?
* what does the literature say on the subject?
* what did you find?

- what do your findings mean?
- how do you explain your results?
- what should be done next?

What are the weaknesses of your research methods?
Are there any weaknesses in your analyses?
How would you correct them?

Summary

- A dissertation is mandatory for most higher university degrees. It is usually based on a piece of research *(see Chapter 12)*.

- A dissertation is an academic monograph on the lines of a research paper, but much longer and thorough in exposition and detail.

- Supervisors are essential in the preparation of dissertations. They decides if the research and dissertation are progressing satisfactorily and if and when you submit the dissertation to examiners.

- Spelling and grammar may decide the outcome of you dissertation.

  Irritate examiners with poor spelling, grating grammatical mistakes and you make them mean (stingy) in awarding marks.

- The dissertation is given a title on a title page, a list of contents, a summary, a boy (the real dissertation), a list of references and the

  appendices before it is ready for examiners' eyes.

- Follow your university's rules on typing, layout of title page, production and numbers of copies to submit.

- If required, prepare well for the oral examination (the inquisition), the defence of your dissertation.

Will you show us your Graduation Video?

Further Reading

1. **Albert T. A-Z of Medical Writing. London:** *BMJ* **Books 2000**

1. Calnan J. **Coping with Research-** *The complete Guide for Beginners.* London: Heinemann 1984.

2. Luey B. **Handbook for Academic Authors.** Cambridge: Cambridge University Press 2002.

3. Watson G. **Writing a Thesis** *-a guide to long essays and dissertations.* London: Longman 1987.

4. Bowling A. **Research Methods in Health.** OUP 2002.

---

14. Using the internet

14.1 A new medium

The internet is fashionable. Businessmen and businesswomen quote their e-mail addresses and *'websites'* on their visiting cards. Heavy goods vehicles, radio and television advertise Web addresses.

Initiation into cyberspace

To the uninitiated, it is frightening and confusing. Can it be learnt from one short chapter? Yes. The principles can be learnt and when the fear has been lifted. It will be easy to talk to colleagues, to ask them to show you how to access e-mail, search the web, how to access to the internet from your own computer or those scattered around hospital library, the wards and all clinical settings.

Once you are connected to the internet you can click onto the *"Help"* button and receive advice. This chapter introduces you to the essentials of internet communications. The adventure is not cheap- not with telephone bills and internet shopping. But I am getting ahead of my story.

14.2 What is the internet?

The internet is a network of computers connected by telephone lines, cables or satellite radio links. The connections may be local- within large organisations or neighbourhoods. They may involve a larger network linking computer systems from several organisations. The connections may span a country, a region or the whole world.

Within the network are *hosts* (large computers with big memory banks) that receive, edit, keep, maintain and distribute electronic data to other computers on demand. Each host has an internet name or *address* that tells other hosts how to find it.

bma.org.uk is the address for the BMA's internet host. The internet address has several parts separated by 'dots'. In this example, the computer called ***bma*** is in the organisation domain *(org)* in the United Kingdom *(uk).*

Countries have been assigned two-letter internet tags, for example **au** for Australia, **az** for South Africa, **de** for Germany, **fr** for France, **in** for India and **uk** for United Kingdom. USA uses **com** for private and business users and **gov** for government internet addresses.

Examples of other host definers:
.co commercial organisation- *the-times.co.uk* (The Times newspaper)
.org public organisations- *bma.org.uk* (British Medical Association)
.ac academic organisations- *wbs.ac.uk* (Warwick Business School)
.gov for government organisations- *doh.gov.uk* (UK DoH)
.int international organisations- *who.inter* (WHO)

Only the last two parts (*ac.az, co.*uk) are determined by the nature and location of the organisation. The choice of other parts of the host name is free although it must be *registered* so that other hosts can find it and are alerted not claim it as their.

14.3 Who created the internet?

The internet was born in 1969 to link computers of the American armed forces, research universities and arms (weapons) manufacturers in USA to ensure that communication between them would continue after nuclear bombing by the former Soviet Union (USSR). Eventually it spread to universities and research organisations outside America. Since 1992 transmitting data on the internet has been much easier and cheap.

The internet can be accessed wherever there is a telephone line (or satellite service) and a computer. It is claimed that digital data transmission and manipulation (the digital revolution) will affect people more than the industrial revolution in Europe did.

14.4 What use is the internet?

The internet is a connection of computers so that they can communicate with each other- like roads connect towns and enable traffic to move between them. The treasures to be enjoyed by surfing the internet (moving from one computer to another) are in the information or data provided by huge host computers.

The variety of information and data accessible range from a simple electronic letter (e-mail) to full multimedia (text, sound, pictures and animation). Anything that can be presented as text, sound or pictures can be transmitted by the internet. The limiting factor is whether or not it has been published on an accessible host?

The following are some of the roles the internet plays in modern economies.

14.4.1 Commerce
Buying and selling goods and services on the internet is growing. Amazon (www.amazon.co.uk) sells books, music CDs, Videos, DVDs and many other products. Charles Schwab (www.schwab-europe.com) deals in stock market shares online (*Online means the telephone line (and satellite radio) is used in exchanging messages*). Many banks have set up online divisions. Most established businesses have internet based marketing and sales departments.

In internet shopping, you select the products you want, pay by credit card through a secure line, place your order and the postman or courier delivers the goods to your door.

Business people use the internet to communicate, to market and distribute products and services. Large businesses communicate with subsidiary units, employees, suppliers, customers, business consultants, trade associations and other groups through the internet (in addition to the traditional telephone, fax, meeting or letter).

Internet shopping is growing and it is often cheaper and more comfortable than walking the streets on a rainy day. You pay by credit cards- hence the need for *internet security.*

14.4.2 Military
The internet was developed to facilitate military communications in USA. National armed forces in advanced countries use secure internet systems to communicate with their forces all over the world.

14.4.3 Publishing research
Researchers are now able to publish on the internet as well as via

traditional journals. They can communicate their findings (and claims to who was first to publish) faster.

Critics say that it encourages premature publication and bypasses traditional peer-review systems. In peer review, recognised experts read and criticise paper before they can be considered for publication. This takes time and some researchers are unhappy about the delay. Others are concerned that a new researcher's work may threaten the older 'expert' and hence bias his or her review of the paper

The internet makes collaboration in research, business, education and crime, easier, faster and cheaper. Questions and problems can be raised, posted, received, and answered quickly.

14.4.4 Education
Teachers are using the internet to assign course work, mark it and advise students on their performance. Students receive course work online and transmit back their efforts. Some universities teach courses partly or wholly online (mailing, teleconferences and discussion groups). Some universities have set up programmes specifically for online students.

How do they ensure that 'the registered student' is the same person who does the work and takes the examinations?

Most of the information you needed for PLAB has been online for many years; it was only after somebody told you that it was where and where to look (web address), that you could download and read it.

14.4.5 Political activity
Candidates for the 2000 USA presidential elections posted their political manifestos on the internet. People visited the websites, read the material and communicated with the candidates' campaign teams by e-mail.

The internet affects the lives of those who have access to it and those who don't too. In Britain many public documents are published online and the public is expected to access them online. If you are connected to the internet, if you know where to look, how to look and when the document was published, you can access, read and study it and respond appropriately. What if you don't?

14.5 Getting onto the internet

If you want to get connected to the internet you need:
* a *computer,* a *modem* and a *telephone line* (or satellite access)
* a suitable *browser* (software to browse or scan internet computers)
* *access* to the internet (via an internet service (access) provider- ISP).

14.5.1 Suitable computer

Your *computer should* have a fast processor, colour screen, adequate free hard disk space to store files (collection of information), adequate working memory (random access memory- RAM) to run software and view messages.

14.5.2 Modem

A modem is a device for connecting your computer, through the telephone line, to an internet service provider. A fast *modem* is essential to reduces the time spent waiting for documents to download. A fast modem reduces telephone bills and access charges- both often charged by the minute. Many internet users have a separate telephone line for internet access.

14.5.3 Modem speeds

The speed of modems is measured in bits per second *(bps).* The slowest is 9600bps (9.6 kbps) and the fastest in common use is 56 kbps (2002).

Faster mechanisms are available. ISDN (Integrated Services Digital Network) is faster but more expensive. Private internet uses are now purchasing ISDN access from telecommunication companies to keep with the need for faster downloading as internet files have become larger. The 56kbps modem is no longer fast enough.

14.5.4 Internet access

Now that you have a suitable computer and a modem you need access to the internet. An service provider (ISP) also known as internet access providers (IAPs) will gladly connect you to the internet. You will be charge for the access and not the connection. Some ISPs (like Yahoo!) charge no access fee provided you use the service regularly- *give them frequent opportunities to show you adverts.*

ISPs advertise their existence and services in newspapers, television and radio. Most ISPs provide free basic software on CD-ROMs or diskettes.

Some allow you to download it from the internet- assuming you have an ISP already! How do you choose an ISP?

14.5.5 Choosing an ISP
For a newcomer, the choice of ISP is confusing. Eventually it comes down to just three questions:
- How fast, reliable and efficient is the ISP?
- How large are their computer databases?
- How expensive is the service?

You want to know if the ISP is fast, reliable and efficient. You want to know that it can handle many inquiries (internet traffic) so that when you want to go online you won't be held in a queue. Messages like *"...the service may be experiencing a lot of traffic. Try again later"* = we are too small to serve you adequately.

What is the quality and size of their database? Check the computer press. Talk to people about their ISPs and why they like them. Are they satisfied with the speed, efficiency and reliability- with the quality of the service they get? How reputable is the ISP? What are the charges for internet access and telephony? Can you afford it? Can you afford to stay off line (do without the internet)?

ISPs provide advice, support software and some security. Large organisations (academic, commercial, administrative, military, governmental, etc.) provide (host) their own internet access. They pay internet companies to establish and maintain the servers. Thus they guarantee a more secure internet access.

14.5.6 The browser
The *browser* is the software (electronic computer codes) that enables you to access the internet. It enables your computer to display pictures *(icons)* on the screen. You select and activate icons by pointing and clicking your computer mouse. The browser scans the internet, locates the information you want and brings it to your computer.

Two browsers dominate the market- Netscape's *Navigator* and Microsoft's *Internet Explorer. Navigator* was the first browser available to the public. It was offered at a low price to commercial users and free to private users.

Netscape invented *Mosaic,* the first browser on the World-Wide Web. *Explorer* is a component of Windows 95, 98, 2000 and later versions of Microsoft's computer operating system.

14.6 Using e-mail

Internet electronic mail (e-mail) allows textual files to be exchanged between internet users. Complex documents are transmissible by special encoding techniques. Modern browsers provide a text editor to remind you to specify the addressee and to give a title to your message.

14.6.1 E-mail addresses

Electronic mail signals pass from senders to recipients. The system must know where to find the electronic document *(file)* to transmit and *where* to find the recipient- the *e-mail address.* Each internet user is assigned an address when he/she buys access from an ISP. Your e-mail address will include your *user name* and the name of your ISP.

Example: *orders@amazon.co.uk* **orders** is the username for the Orders department at Amazon, @ pronounced as 'at' (located at) *amazon.co.uk* the ISP for Amazon, UK.

Your e-mail address is derived from your names (or company name) or whatever you want it be, and the name of your ISP. Let us pretend that:
• your name is *A. Kumar* and
• your internet service provider is *rapid.co.uk*

Your e-mail address might be *Kumar@ rapid.co.uk* or *AKuma@ rapid.co.uk;* or whatever combination of letters and numeral you choose.

People with common surnames *(Smith, Schmidt, Khalid, Jones, Kumar, Mukasa, Kamau, etc.)* frequently find that somebody else has already registered their name in an e-mail address with the ISP. So they include initials and even numerals in their e-mail addresses. Using initials and numerals increases the number of user names and choice of e-mail addresses.

14.6.2 Sending and receiving e-mail

Sending and receiving e-mails is surprisingly simple- just clicking your computer mouse on icons or words on your monitor's screen. The ISP servers forward your electronic messages to machines on the internet.

Servers (large computers) direct packets of the message onwards and reassemble them at the server specified by the address in the message. ISP servers store the electronic mail till asked for it.

When you register with an ISP, an e-mail will welcome you. You wouldn't expect them to send you a letter by Royal Mail, would you?

After connecting to the internet, you may send e-mails to friends, professional and business contacts to announce your arrival into cyberspace.

Internet browsers automatically give transmission details at the recipient's end. The following is the beginning of an e-mail I received on 30 September 2002 about a delayed computer purchase:

> *From: Sonia_Hogan@Dell.com*
> *To: ebturya@yahoo.co.uk*
> *Subject: Computer purchase - not delivered- where is it?*
> *Date: Mon, 30 Sep 2002 03:07:27 -0500*

If a message is returned, reason(s) for the failure of delivery are given- like a good postal system should do!

14.6.3 Composing an e-mail
You should be as careful in writing e-mails as you are with letters. You should be diligent with spelling, grammar and the tone of the message. One mouse click and you have transmitted misspelled words or rude messages. Edit your message before sending it- use the spellchecker.

In business, friendship and love affairs, e-mail is as important as letters. E-mail may appear as informal as a telephone conversation- *but it is recorded!* The message could infer a contract for business or a marriage offer. Be careful- it will be recorded and kept for sometime.

14.6.4 Legal status of e-mail
In law e-mail has the same status as written documents. It can be used as

evidence in a court of law. Make sure your e-mail does not compromise you and your business.

In 1998-99, when Microsoft was sued for monopolistic behaviour towards corporate customers and competitors, e-mail from the company's computers was accepted as evidence by the trial judge.

14.6.5 E-mail etiquette
You should be aware of the way external users read and appreciate e-mail. Are there any formal rules?

E-mail is less formal than letters. The exchange is not hampered by conventions of written business letters. Nevertheless e-mail conventions has evolved. They are quite important to newsgroups, facilitate communication and avoid offence.

Lower case letters are used to write e-mail, unless you want to SHOUT. Shouting is taken a sign of anger. Use lower case letters unless you are angry and want to SHOUT.

Unsolicited e-mail is not welcomed. Internauts pay the ISP and for telephone time to download the message. Unsolicited e-mail is annoying particularly if long, unwanted, or worse, useless *commercial* messages. Unlike unsolicited paper mail, you can't throw it away before opening it!

14.6.6 Business e-mail
It is relatively easy to transmit complex documents quickly, securely and cheaply by e-mail. It is a useful business tool (like letters, faxes, telephone calls and personal meetings).

14.6.7 Accessing newsgroups
When many people receive the same message, the e-mail fills the role of a group letter. The internet allows exchanges within larger discussion groups *or 'newsgroups'.* Any member of the group may post topics, comment on current subjects or on subjects previously posted or post new topics.

Usually the group has a common pursuit, a hobby, profession, a social or religious association or some other interest. Most medical royal colleges and subspecialty groups host discussion groups.

In some newsgroups, a *moderator* acts as editor and runs the group. However most newsgroups are free-form with no control other than that users impose on themselves.

14.6.8 News on the internet
It is easy to access and read news and comment on current issues via the internet. Articles may be linked to other related items and to articles previously posted. I use the internet to search for articles about medicine, business, politics and my roots.

14.7 The World Wide Web
The World Wide Web (the Web, WWW) is a network of powerful computers around the world. It became possible in 1992, when Tim Bernes-Lee and Robert Cailliau, physicists at the European Laboratory for Particle Physics (CERN) in Switzerland developed, and posted free, essential parts of hypertext system-HTTP (HyperText Transport Protocol), HTML (HyperText Mark Language), and URL (Uniform Resource Locator). No charge was made for their use.

HTTP allows Web browsers to communicate with servers. HTML is the language in which Web pages are written. URL provides the addresses for Web pages and other information on the internet. These protocols enable fast multimedia information exchanges.

On the Web information is structured into *pages.* The pages may contain a variety of data formats:
* structured (formatted) text with titles, headings, highlights, etc
* pictures and colourful animations *(moving* pictures)
* *sounds-* spoken words to full musical effects
* links (hypertext) to related topics within the website
* forms that may be completed and electronically mailed.

14.7.1 How does it work?
Page links create a 'web, or network of interconnected pages (website). The links are called 'hypertext.' Every website has a *'location' in* the Web specified by a **uniform resource locator** (URL). The URL, the address quoted by advertisers, provides a means of locating information on the internet.

An URL has two parts, the address of the host on which it is stored and the location of the file on an ISP's system. The BMJ website is www.bmj.com. You would type http://www.bmj.com into the address line of your browser to visit the site. To the basic URL can be added extensions separated by '/' to specify particular pages on the website.

If I wanted information about membership of the BMA I would access the BMA website by typing http://www.bma.org.uk/membership into the browser on my screen. The inquiry would go to *bma.org.uk* and seek out *membership*, the Web pages for BMA membership would then be displayed on my computer screen.

In addition to http, there are other protocols used in configuring internet data transfers. html (hypertext mark-up language) describes the pages and ftp (file transfer protocol) transfers files in cyberspace.

14.7.2 Searching the Web
There are information seams on the internet waiting for you to mine them for your benefit. You should keep a record of URLs with material relevant to your professional, educational and personal interests so that you can visit them as needed.
It takes a long time to find relevant material by simply surfing-moving from link to link. Knowing the URL saves time and telephone costs.

Catalogues of frequently visited websites exist. Many popular magazines and journals published an internet version. They quote their URL on the printed version of the journal.

14.7.3 Searching the internet
Netscape and Explorer provide links to popular search engines like *Yahoo, Excite, Magellan and Google*. Search engines are web servers with *very* large databases- millions of Web pages. They regularly explore the Web for new informative pages to update and expand their databases. The best search engines carefully index the material, and may provide an editorial comment on the quality of the site.

Search engines have a text box for search terms (the word or phrase) you are interested in. The search engine will *rank* search terms according to how frequently they appear in Web pages. It will present a list of the terms and their URLs. What you want may be at the end of a long list.

14.7.4 Accessing websites
Usually accessing a *website* is simple; the browser displays Web pages with hypertext links so that you can move from page to page and back as required.

Some sites, restrict access and may ask you to pay *(by credit card)* before you enter the website and read, download or print the material.

Often even free websites ask you to *'Register'* (give information about yourself), which is useful in marketing efforts by related organisations.

14.8 Downloading files
The internet enables you to access and download files from host systems around the world. Your browser will guide you.

14.9 Internet threatens order
The Internet is a threat to postal and telecommunications businesses. It is changing the way business is done in education, entertainment, news media and communications industries:
* in newspaper, magazine, music and book publishing the internet is faster and cheaper

* in continuing adult education, larger and disperse audiences can be reached more cheaply, and a wider choice of courses and activities offered. Lecturers and tutorial staff will lose jobs.

* in financial services (banking, mortgages lending, insurance, share trading), the internet enables a wider and cheaper ranges of services than traditional providers.

* television, video, films and music production, transmission and marketing have been revolutionised by electronic communications.

Even if you are not in business, the internet is invaluable for keeping in touch with friends and colleagues, in work, education and leisure, quickly and cheaply.

14.10 Computer viruses
Computer viruses are endemic on the internet. Before getting established and before downloading program, you should install effective anti-virus software. You should regularly:
- copy important information and keep it away from the computer
- up-date your antivirus software to cover new viruses.

14.11 Internet security
To facility commerce on the internet, customer's credit card numbers must be transmitted safely. *Encryption* was included in browsers to prevent theft. The information is scrambled before it is transmitted so that, even if it is stolen, it can not be read by the thief.

Summary
- the internet, a network of computers that exchanges information, was born in USA in 1969 to ensure communication between the armed forces, and research universities in the event nuclear bombing by the USSR

- the creation of *http, html,* and *url* established the Web (WWW)

- internet conventions govern the designation of e-mail addresses, and websites

- it is accessed with a computer, a modem, an ISP, a telephone line and a browser

- multimedia (text, sound, colour pictures, animation) messages can be exchanged on the Web

- it is useful for commercial, educational, military, recreational political, religious and social exchanges of information
- computer viruses can spread rapidly via the internet and antivirus software is now essential

- the Web supports websites that are visited, browsed and downloaded as appropriate
- e-mail has the same legal status as written documents

- encryption ensures the security and confidentiality of transmitted messages.

Further Reading

1. Preston Gralla. **How the Internet works**. Que Corporation 2001. *an excellent schematic introduction to the internet and the Web*

2. Richard Wentk.**The Which? guide to the Internet**. Which? Books 2001. *A good introduction to the Internet.*

Index

Epilogue

Has *'Your Career after PLAB'* helped you find a clinical attachment, apply for jobs or handle interviews? Has *it* shown you how to write curricula vitae, clinical letters and reports, research papers for publication and a dissertation for a higher degree? Will you be more confident at your next job interviews?

Are there some topics you would like covered in a future edition of this book? Please let me know how *'Your Career after PLAB'* could be improved.

info@edukom.co.uk